LULLY, *lulla, thou little tiny child,*
By by, lully lullay.
O sisters too,
How may we do
For to preserve this day
This poor youngling,
For whom we do sing,
By by, lully lullay?

Herod, the king,
In his raging,
Chargèd he hath this day
His men of might,
In his own sight,
All young childrén to slay.

That woe is me,
Poor child for thee!
And ever morn and day,
For thy parting
Neither say nor sing
By by, lully lullay!

The
COVENTRY CAROL

Pageant of the Shearmen and Tailors

15th Century

To

From

THE CHRISTMAS BOOK ✳ THE CHRISTMAS BOOK ✳ THE CHRISTMAS BOOK ✳ THE CHRISTMAS BOOK ✳ THE CHRISTMAS BOOK ✳

THE CHRISTMAS BOOK

EDITED BY

Harry Ballam

and

Phyllis Digby Morton

SAMPSON LOW

MADE AND PRINTED IN GREAT BRITAIN BY PURNELL AND SONS, LTD.,
PAULTON (SOMERSET) AND LONDON

Foreword

LIKE Christmas pudding, THE CHRISTMAS BOOK is a rich and peculiar mixture, for 'rich and peculiar' is surely an accurate description of a work that includes papers by writers as different, say, as Osbert Sitwell, Nathaniel Gubbins and the Dean of St. Paul's, and fiction by authors as divergent as William Sansom and Bram Stoker. Very naturally, it is the pious hope of the editors that, like a good Christmas pudding, the book will prove popular seasonable fare, but whether the ingredients do indeed add up to an ideal recipe the reader will judge for him- or herself. To borrow a cracker motto from one of the section title-pages, 'The proof of the pudding . . .'

A very considerable part of the matter in THE CHRISTMAS BOOK has been written specially for it and appears in print for the first time, the remainder being reprinted from the works of contemporary and a few past authors. There are sound reasons for this apparently inconsistent method of compilation. The intention of the editors has been to produce a miscellany, widely comprehensive on the curiously fascinating subject of Christmas and, where there were papers in existence that dealt admirably with a particular aspect, they sought to include them but ruled out those which, however brilliant, were likely to be too familiar to the general reader; other aspects still, it seemed, had never been adequately covered in a form suitable for presentation here so that, one way and another, many gaps remained in the structure of the book and those contemporary writers whom the editors felt would most notably fill them, were invited to do so.

Of the specific contents of the book there is little to be said. The editors have again failed to subscribe to the convention of modern English miscellanies by including the Americans; nineteenth-century America is represented by Washington Irving (without whom no Christmas book would be complete) and Charlotte Perkins Gilman, while two of their contemporary writers have provided fresh papers. In choice of fiction, however, convention has been strictly observed and the short stories printed, though they do not conform to the types laid down by Miss Laski in her satirical essay here, at least adhere to Christmas tradition in subject. In deference also to a prevalent taste (which, it must be admitted, is entirely shared by the editors) the book includes several quizzes.

A great many people assisted the editors in their task and to all of them acknowledgements are due. First and foremost of these is Edgar Ballard who forsook his paintings to devote a considerable amount of time to art editing the book. He is responsible for the dust-jacket decorated with Victorian scraps, the cover, and the design and typography throughout the book, as well as certain of the illustrations. A number of artists decorated the text, including Terry Freeman, Leonard Rosoman, Pearl Falconer, Nancy Innes, and Barbara Jones (named in the order of their first appearance in the book). Of the many nineteenth-century works from which woodcuts and decorations have been culled, the most prolific source was an illustrious predecessor published a hundred years ago by Ingram Cooke & Co., who were closely associated with *The Illustrated London News*.

For permission to reprint various copyright essays and stories the editors have to thank Sir Osbert Sitwell and Messrs. Macmillan for ' Still Life: Box and Bottle ', abridged, of necessity, from his book *Sing High! Sing Low!;* Messrs. Chatto & Windus for ' New-Fashioned Christmas ' from *The Olive Tree;* Messrs. George Routledge for ' The Judge's House ' from *Dracula's Guest;* and the editor of *The Sunday Express* for ' A Christmas Bill '. The music of the carols printed on the endpapers is reproduced from *The Oxford Book of Carols* by permission of the Oxford University Press.

Every possible effort has been made to trace the owners of doubtful copyrights of reprinted text and reproduced drawings and if, unwittingly, any infringement has nevertheless occurred, editors and publisher tender their apologies.

H. B.
P. D. M.

Contents

7

The Spirit of Christmas

Welcome the coming, speed the parting guest
Exchange of gifts makes good friends
Happy men shall have many friends
Give and spend and God will send

A Christmas Tree

BY CHARLES DICKENS

I HAVE BEEN looking on, this evening, at a merry company of children assembled round that pretty German toy, a Christmas Tree. The tree was planted in the middle of a great round table, and towered high above our heads. It was brilliantly lighted by a multitude of little tapers; and everywhere sparkled and glittered with bright objects. There were rosy-cheeked dolls, hiding behind the green leaves; and there were real watches (with movable hands, at least, and an endless capacity of being wound up) dangling from innumerable twigs; there were French-polished tables, chairs, bedsteads, wardrobes, eight-day clocks, and various other articles of domestic furniture (wonderfully made, in tin, at Wolverhampton), perched among the boughs, as if in preparation for some fairy housekeeping; there were jolly, broad-faced little men, much more agreeable in appearance than many real men—and no wonder, for their heads took off, and showed them to be full of sugarplums; there were fiddles and drums; there were tambourines, books, work-boxes, paint-boxes, sweetmeat-boxes, peepshow-boxes, and all kinds of boxes; there were trinkets for the elder girls, far brighter than any grown-up gold or jewels; there were baskets and pin-cushions in all devices; there were guns, swords, and banners; there were witches standing in enchanted rings of pasteboard, to tell fortunes; there were teetotums, humming-tops, needle cases, pen-wipers, smelling-bottles, conversation-cards, bouquet-holders; real fruit, made artificially dazzling with gold leaf; imitation apples, pears, and walnuts, crammed with surprises; in short, as a pretty child, before me, delightedly whispered to another pretty child, her bosom friend, 'There was everything, and more'. This motley collection of odd objects, clustering on the tree like magic fruit, and flashing back the bright looks directed towards it on every side—some of the diamond-eyes admiring it were hardly on a level with the table, and a few were languishing in timid wonder on the bosoms of pretty mothers, aunts, and nurses—made a lively realisation of the fancies of childhood; and set me thinking how all the trees that grow and all the things that come into existence on the earth, have their wild adornments at that well-remembered time.

Being now at home again, and alone, the only person in the house awake, my thoughts are drawn back, by a fascination which I do not care to resist, to my own childhood. I begin to consider, what do we all remember best upon the branches of the Christmas Tree of our own young Christmas days, by which we climbed to real life.

Straight, in the middle of the room, cramped in the freedom of its growth by no encircling walls or soon-reached ceiling, a shadowy tree arises; and, looking up into the dreamy brightness of its top—for I observed in this tree the singular property that it appears to grow down-ward towards the earth—I look into my youngest Christmas recol-lections!

All toys at first, I find. Up yonder, among the green holly and red berries, is the Tumbler with his hands in his pockets, who wouldn't lie down, but whenever he was put upon the floor, persisted in rolling his fat body about, until he rolled himself still, and brought those lobster eyes of his to bear upon me—when I affected to laugh very much, but in my heart of hearts was extremely doubtful of him. Close beside him is that infernal snuff-box, out of which there sprang a demoniacal Counsellor in a black gown, with an obnoxious head of hair, and a red cloth mouth, wide open, who was not to be endured on any terms, but could not be put away either; for he used suddenly, in a highly magnified state, to fly out of Mammoth Snuff-boxes in dreams, when least expected. Nor is the frog with cobbler's wax on his tail, far off; for there was no knowing where he wouldn't jump, and when he flew over the candle, and came upon one's hand with that spotted back—red on a green ground—he was horrible. The cardboard lady in a blue-silk skirt, who was stood up against the candlestick to dance, and whom I see on the same branch, was milder, and was beautiful; but I can't say as much for the larger cardboard man, who used to be hung against the wall and pulled by a string; there was a sinister expression in that nose of his; and when he got his legs round his neck (which he very often did), he was ghastly, and not a creature to be alone with.

When did that dreadful Mask first look at me? Who put it on, and why was I so frightened that the sight of it is an era in my life? It is not a hideous visage in itself; it is even meant to be droll; why then were its stolid features so intolerable? Surely not because it hid the wearer's face. An apron would have done as much; and though I should have preferred even the apron away, it would not have been absolutely insupportable, like the mask. Was it the immovability of the mask? The doll's face was immovable, but I was not afraid of *her*. Perhaps that fixed and set change coming over a real face, infused into my quickened heart some remote suggestion and dread of the universal change that is to come on every face, and make it still? Nothing reconciled me to it. No drummers, from whom proceeded a melancholy chirping on the turning of a handle; no regiment of soldiers, with a mute band, taken out of a box and fitted, one by one, upon a stiff and lazy little set of lazy-tongs; no old woman, made of wires and a brown-paper composition, cutting up a pie for two small children, could give me a permanent comfort, for a long time. Nor was it any satisfaction to be shown the Mask, and see that it was made of paper, or to have it locked up and be assured that no one wore it. The mere recollection of that fixed face, the mere knowledge of its existence anywhere, was sufficient to wake me in the night all perspiration and horror, with, ' O I know it's coming! O the mask! '

I never wondered what the dear old donkey with the panniers— there he is!—was made of, then! His hide was real to the touch, I recollect. And the great black horse with the round red spots all over him—the horse that I could even get upon—I never wondered what had brought him to that strange condition, or thought that such a horse was not commonly seen at Newmarket. The four horses of no colour, next to him, that went into the wagon of cheeses, and could be taken out and stabled under the piano, appear to have bits of fur-tippet for their tails, and other bits for their manes, and to stand on pegs instead of legs, but it was not so when they were brought home for a Christmas present. They were all right, then; neither was their harness unceremoniously nailed into their chests, as appears to be the case now. The tinkling works of the music-cart, I *did* find out, to be made of quill tooth-picks and wire; and I always thought that little Tumbler in shirt sleeves, perpetually swarming up one side of a wooden frame, and coming down, head foremost, on the other, rather a weak-minded person—though good-natured; but the Jacob's Ladder, next to him, made of little squares of red wood, that went flapping and clattering over one another, each developing a different picture, and the whole enlivened by small bells, was a mighty marvel and a great delight.

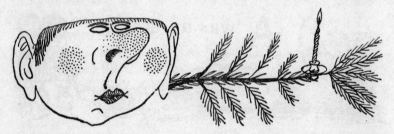

Ah! The Doll's House!—of which I was not proprietor, but where I visited. I don't admire the Houses of Parliament half so much as that stone-fronted mansion with real glass windows, and door-steps, and a real balcony—greener than I ever see now, except at watering places; and even they afford but a poor imitation. And though it *did* open all at once, the entire house-front (which was a blow, I admit, as cancelling the fiction of a staircase), it was but to shut it up again, and I could believe. Even open, there were three distinct rooms in it: a sitting-room and bedroom, elegantly furnished, and best of all, a kitchen, with uncommonly soft fire-irons, a plentiful assortment of diminutive utensils—oh, the warming-pan!—and a tin man-cook in profile, who was always going to fry two fish. What Barmecide justice have I done to the noble feasts wherein the set of wooden platters figured, each with its own peculiar delicacy, as a ham or turkey, glued tight on to it, and garnished with something green, which I recollect as moss! Could all the Temperance Societies of these later days, united, give me such a tea-drinking as I have had through the means of yonder little set of blue crockery, which really would hold liquid (it ran out of the small wooden cask, I recollect, and tasted of matches), and which made tea, nectar. And if the two legs of the ineffectual little sugar-tongs did tumble over one another, and want purpose, like Punch's hands, what does it matter? And if I did once shriek out, as a poisoned child, and strike the fashionable company with consternation, by reason of having drunk a little teaspoon, inadvertently dissolved in too hot tea, I was never the worst for it, except by a powder!

Upon the next branches of the tree, lower down, hard by the green roller and miniature gardening-tools, how thick the books begin to hang. Thin books, in themselves, at first, but many of them, and with deliciously smooth covers of bright red or green. With fat black letters

to begin with! 'A was an archer, and shot at a frog.' Of course he was. He was an apple-pie also, and there he is! He was a good many things in his time, was A, and so were most of his friends, except X, who had so little versatility, that I never knew him to get beyond Xerxes or Xantippe—like Y, who was always confined to a Yacht or a Yew Tree; and Z condemned for ever to be a Zebra or a Zany. But, now, the very tree itself changes, and becomes a bean-stalk—the marvellous bean-stalk up which Jack climbed to the Giant's house! And now, those dreadfully interesting, double-headed giants, with their clubs over their shoulders, begin to stride along the boughs in a perfect throng, dragging knights and ladies home for dinner by the hair of their heads. And Jack—how noble, with his sword of sharpness, and his shoes of swiftness! Again those old meditations come upon me as I gaze up at him; and I debate within myself whether there was more than one Jack (which I am loth to believe possible), or only one genuine original admirable Jack, who achieved all the recorded exploits.

Good for Christmas-time is the ruddy colour of the cloak, in which —the tree making a forest of itself for her to trip through, with her basket—Little Red Riding-Hood comes to me one Christmas Eve to give me information of the cruelty and treachery of that dissembling Wolf who ate her grandmother, without making any impression on his appetite, and then ate her, after making that ferocious joke about his teeth. She was my first love. I felt that if I could have married Little Red Riding-Hood, I should have known perfect bliss. But, it was not to be; and there was nothing for it but to look out the Wolf in the Noah's Ark there, and put him late in the procession on the table, as a monster who was to be degraded. O the wonderful Noah's Ark! it was not found seaworthy when put in a washtub, and the animals were crammed in at the roof, and needed to have their legs well shaken

down before they could be got in, even there—and then, ten to one but they began to tumble out at the door, which was but imperfectly fastened with a wire latch—but what was *that* against it! Consider the noble fly, a size or two smaller than the elephant: the lady-bird, the butterfly—all triumphs of art! Consider the goose, whose feet were so small, and whose balance was so indifferent, that he usually tumbled forward, and knocked down all the animal creation. Consider Noah and his family, like idiotic tobacco-stoppers; and how the leopard stuck to warm little fingers; and how the tails of the larger animals used gradually to resolve themselves into frayed bits of string!

Hush! Again a forest, and somebody up in a tree—not Robin Hood, not Valentine, not the Yellow Dwarf (I have passed him and all Mother Bunch's wonders, without mention), but an Eastern King with a glittering scimitar and turban. By Allah! two Eastern Kings, for I see another, looking over his shoulder! Down upon the grass, at the tree's foot, lies the full length of a coal-black Giant, stretched asleep, with his head in a lady's lap; and near them is a glass box, fastened with four locks of shining steel, in which he keeps the lady prisoner when he is awake. I see the four keys at his girdle now. The lady makes signs to the two kings in the tree, who softly descend. It is the setting-in of the bright Arabian Nights.

Oh, now all common things become uncommon and enchanted to me. All lamps are wonderful; all rings are talismans. Common flower-pots are full of treasure, with a little earth scattered on the top; trees are for Ali Baba to hide in; beef-steaks are to throw down into the Valley of Diamonds, that the precious stones may stick to them, and be carried by the eagles to their nests, whence the traders, with loud cries, will scare them. Tarts are made, according to the recipe of the Vizier's son of Bussorah, who turned pastrycook after he was set down in his drawers at the gate of Damascus; cobblers are all Mustaphas, and in

the habit of sewing up people cut in four pieces, to whom they are taken blindfold.

Any iron ring let into stone is the entrance to a cave which only waits for the magician, and the little fire, and the necromancy, that will make the earth shake. All the dates imported come from the same tree as that unlucky date, with whose shell the merchant knocked out the eye of the genie's invisible son. All olives are of the stock of that fresh fruit, concerning which the Commander of the Faithful over-heard the boy conduct the fictitious trial of the fraudulent olive mer-chant; all apples are akin to the apple purchased (with two others) from the Sultan's gardener for three sequins, and which the tall black slave stole from the child. All dogs are associated with the dog, really a transformed man, who jumped upon the baker's counter, and put his paw on the piece of bad money. All rice recalls the rice which the awful lady, who was a ghoul, could only peck by grains, because of her nightly feasts in the burial-place. My very rocking-horse—there he is, with his nostrils turned completely inside-out, indicative of Blood!—should have a peg in his neck, by virtue thereof to fly away with me, as the wooden horse did with the Prince of Persia, in the sight of all his father's court.

Yes, on every object that I recognise among those upper branches of my Christmas Tree, I see this fairy light! When I wake in bed, at daybreak, on the cold, dark, winter mornings, the white snow dimly beheld, outside, through the frost on the windowpane, I hear Dinarzade. ' Sister, sister, if you are yet awake, I pray you finish the history of the Young King of the Black Islands.' Scheherazade replies, ' If my lord the Sultan will suffer me to live another day, sister, I will not only finish that, but tell you a more wonderful story yet.' Then, the gracious Sultan goes out, giving no orders for the execution, and we all three breathe again.

At this height of my tree I begin to see, cowering among the leaves —it may be born of turkey, or of pudding, or mince pie, or of these many fancies, jumbled with Robinson Crusoe on his desert island, Phillip Quarll among the monkeys, Sandford and Merton with Mr. Barlow, Mother Bunch, and the Mask—or it may be the result of indigestion, assisted by imagination and over-doctoring—a prodigious nightmare. It is so exceedingly indistinct, that I don't know why it's frightful—but I know it is. I can only make out that it is an immense array of shapeless things, which appear to be planted on a vast exaggeration of the lazy-tongs that used to bear the toy soldiers, and to be slowly coming close to my eyes, and receding to an immeasurable distance. When it comes closest, it is worse. In connection with it I descry remembrances of winter nights incredibly long; of being sent early to bed, as a punishment for some small offence, and waking in two hours, with a sensation of having been asleep two nights; of the laden hopelessness of morning ever dawning; and the oppression of a weight of remorse.

And now, I see a wonderful row of little lights rise smoothly out of the ground, before a vast green curtain. Now, a bell rings—a magic bell, which still sounds in my ears unlike all other bells—and music plays, amidst a buzz of voices, and a fragrant smell of orange peel and oil. Anon, the magic bell commands the music to cease, and the great green curtain rolls itself up majestically, and The Play begins! The devoted dog of Montargis avenges the death of his master, foully murdered in the Forest of Bondy; and a humorous Peasant with a red nose and a very little hat, whom I take from this hour forth to my bosom as a friend (I think he was a Waiter or an Hostler at a village Inn, but many years have passed since he and I have met), remarks that the sassigassity of that dog is indeed surprising; and evermore this jocular conceit will live in my remembrance fresh and unfading, over-

topping all possible jokes, unto the end of time. Or now, I learn with bitter tears how poor Jane Shore, dressed all in white, and with her brown hair hanging down, went starving through the streets; or how George Barnwell killed the worthiest uncle that man ever had, and was afterwards so sorry for it that he ought to have been let off. Comes swift to comfort me, the Pantomime—stupendous Phenomenon!— when clowns are shot from loaded mortars into the great chandelier, bright constellation that it is; when Harlequins, covered all over with scales of pure gold, twist and sparkle, like amazing fish; when Pantaloon (whom I deem it no irreverence to compare in my own mind to my grandfather) puts red-hot pokers in his pocket, and cries ' Here's somebody coming! ' or taxes the Clown with petty larceny, by saying, ' Now, I sawed you do it! ' when Everything is capable, with the greatest of ease, of being changed into Anything; and ' Nothing is, but thinking makes it so.' Now, too, I perceive my first experience of the dreary sensation—often to return in after-life—of being unable, next day, to get back to the dull, settled world; of wanting to live in the bright atmosphere I have quitted; of doting on the little Fairy, with a wand like a celestial Barber's Pole, and pining for a Fairy immortality along with her. Ah, she comes back in many shapes, as my eye wanders down the branches of my Christmas Tree, and goes as often, and has never yet stayed by me!

Out of this delight springs the toy-theatre—there it is, with its familiar proscenium, and ladies in feathers, in the boxes!—and all its attendant occupation with paste and glue, and gum, and water colours, in the getting-up of the Miller and his Men, and Elizabeth, or the Exile of Siberia. In spite of a few besetting accidents and failures (particularly an unreasonable disposition in the respectable Kelmar, and some others, to become faint in the legs, and double up, at exciting points of the drama), a teeming world of fancies so suggestive and

all-embracing, that, far below it on my Christmas Tree, I see dark, dirty, real Theatres in the daytime, adorned with these associations as with the freshest garlands of the rarest flowers, and charming me yet.

But hark! The Waits are playing, and they break my childish sleep! What images do I associate with the Christmas music as I see them set forth on the Christmas Tree? Known before all the others, keeping far apart from all the others, they gather round my little bed. An angel, speaking to a group of shepherds in a field; some travellers, with eyes uplifted, following a star; a baby in a manger; a child in a spacious temple, talking with grave men; a solemn figure, with a mild and beautiful face, raising a dead girl by the hand; again, near a city gate, calling back the son of a widow, on his bier, to life; a crowd of people looking through the open roof of the chamber where he sits, and letting down a sick person on a bed, with ropes; the same, in a tempest, walking on the water to a ship; again, on a sea-shore, teaching a great multitude; again, with a child upon his knee, and other children round; again, restoring sight to the blind, speech to the dumb, hearing to the deaf, health to the sick, strength to the lame, knowledge to the ignorant; again, dying upon a Cross, watched by armed soldiers, a thick darkness coming on, the earth beginning to shake, and only one voice heard, ' Forgive them, for they know not what they do'.

Still, on the lower and maturer branches of the Tree, Christmas associations cluster thick. School-books shut up; Ovid and Virgil silenced; the Rule of Three, with its cool impertinent inquiries, long disposed of; Terence and Plautus acted no more, in an arena of huddled desks and forms, all chipped, and notched, and inked; trodden grass and the softened noise of shouts in the evening air; the tree is still fresh, still gay. If I no more come home at Christmas-time, there will be boys and girls (thank Heaven!) while the world lasts; and they do!

Yonder they dance and play upon the branches of my Tree, God bless them, merrily, and my heart dances and plays too!

And I *do* come home at Christmas. We all do, or we all should. We all come home, or ought to come home for a short holiday—the longer the better—from the great boarding-school, where we are for ever working at our arithmetical slates, to take, and give a rest. As to going a-visiting, where can we not go, if we will; where have we not been, when we would; starting our fancy from our Christmas Tree!

Away into the winter prospect. There are many such upon the tree! On, by low-lying, misty grounds, through fens and fogs, up long hills, winding dark as caverns between thick plantations, almost shutting out the sparkling stars; so, out on broad heights, until we stop at last, with sudden silence at an avenue. The gate-bell has a deep, half-awful sound in the frosty air; the gate swings open on its hinges; and, as we drive up to the great house, the glancing lights grow larger in the windows, and the opposing rows of trees seem to fall solemnly back on either side, to give us place. At intervals, all day, a frightened hare has shot across this whitened turf; or the distant clatter of a herd of deer trampling the hard frost, has, for the moment, crushed the silence too. Their watchful eyes beneath the fern may be shining now, if we could see them, like the icy dewdrops on the leaves; but they are still, and all is still. And so, the lights growing larger, and the trees falling back before us, and closing up again behind us, as if to forbid retreat, we come to the house.

There is probably a smell of roast chestnuts and other good comfortable things all the time, for we are telling Winter Stories—Ghost Stories, or more shame for us—round the Christmas fire; and we have never stirred except to draw a little nearer to it. But, no matter for that. We came to the house, and it is an old house, full of great chimneys where wood is burnt on ancient dogs upon the hearth, and

grim portraits (some of them with grim legends, too) lower distrustfully from the oaken panels of the walls. We are a middle-aged nobleman, and we make a generous supper with our host and hostess and their guests—it being Christmas-time, and the old house full of company— and then we go to bed. Our room is a very old room. It is hung with tapestry. We don't like the portrait of the cavalier in green, over the fire-place. There are great black beams in the ceiling, and there is a great black bedstead, supported at the foot by two great black figures, who seem to have come off a couple of tombs in the old baronial church in the park, for our particular accommodation. But, we are not a superstitious nobleman, and we do not mind. Well! we dismiss our servant, lock the door, and sit before the fire in our dressing-gown, musing about a great many things. At length we go to bed. Well! we can't sleep. We toss and tumble, and can't sleep. The embers on the hearth burn fitfully and make the room look ghostly. We can't help peeping out over the counterpane, at the two black figures and the cavalier—that wicked-looking cavalier—in green. In the flickering light they seem to advance and retire: which, though we are not by any means a superstitious nobleman, is not agreeable.

Well! we get nervous—more and more nervous. We say ' This is very foolish, but we can't stand this; we'll pretend to be ill, and knock up somebody.' Well! we are just going to do it, when the locked door opens, and there comes in a young woman, deadly pale, and with long fair hair, who glides to the fire, and sits down in the chair we have left there, wringing her hands. Then we notice that her clothes are wet. Our tongue cleaves to the roof of our mouth, and we can't speak; but we observe her accurately. Her clothes are wet; her long hair is dabbled with moist mud; she is dressed in the fashion of two hundred years ago; and she has at her girdle a rusty bunch of keys. Well! there she sits, and we can't even faint, we are in such a state about it.

Presently she gets up, and tries all the locks in the room with the rusty keys, which won't fit one of them; then, she fixes her eyes on the portrait of the cavalier in green, and says, in a low, terrible voice, ' The stags know it!' After that, she wrings her hands again, passes the bedside and goes out at the door. We hurry on our dressing-gown, seize our pistols (we always travel with pistols), and are following when we find the door locked. We turn the key, look out into the dark gallery; no one there. We wander away and try to find our servant. Can't be done. We pace the gallery till daybreak; then return to our deserted room, fall asleep, and are awakened by our servant (nothing ever haunts *him*) and the shining sun. Well! we make a wretched breakfast, and all the company say we look queer.

After breakfast, we go over the house with our host, and then we take him to the portrait of the cavalier in green, and then it all comes out. He was false to a young house-keeper once attached to the family, and famous for her beauty, who drowned herself in a pond, and whose body was discovered after a long time, because the stags refused to drink of the water. Since which, it has been whispered that she traverses the house at midnight (but goes especially to that room where the cavalier was wont to sleep), trying the old locks with the rusty keys. Well! we tell our host of what we have seen, and a shade comes over his features, and he begs it may be hushed up; and so it is. But, it's all true; and we said so, before we died (we are dead now) to many responsible people.

There is no end to the old houses, with resounding galleries and dismal state-chambers, and haunted wings shut up for many years, through which we may ramble with an agreeable creeping up our back, and encounter any number of ghosts, but (it is worthy of remark perhaps) reducible to a very few general types and classes; for, ghosts have little originality, and ' walk ' in a beaten track. Thus, it comes

to pass, that a certain room in a certain old hall, where a certain bad lord, baronet, knight, or gentleman, shot himself, has certain planks in the floor from which the blood *will not* be taken out. You may scrape and scrape, as the present owner has done, or plane and plane, as his father did, or scrub and scrub as his grandfather did, or burn and burn with strong acids as his great-grandfather did, but there the blood will still be—no redder and no paler—no more and no less— always just the same. Thus, in such another house there is a haunted door, that never will keep open; or another door that never will keep shut; or a haunted sound of a spinning wheel, or a hammer, or a foot-step, or a cry, or a sigh, or a horse's tramp, or the rattling of a chain. Or else, there is a turret-clock, which, at the midnight hour, strikes thirteen when the head of the family is going to die; or a shadowy, immovable black carriage which at such a time is always seen by some-body, waiting near the great gates in the stable-yard. Or thus, it came to pass how Lady Mary went to pay a visit at a large wild house in the Scottish Highlands, and, being fatigued with her long journey, retired to bed early, and innocently said, next morning, at the breakfast table, ' How odd, to have so late a party last night, in this remote place, and not to tell me of it, before I went to bed! ' Then, every one asked Lady Mary what she meant? Then, Lady Mary replied, ' Why, all night long, the carriages were driving round and round the terrace, underneath my window! ' Then, the owner of the house turned pale, and so did his Lady, and Charles Macdoodle of Macdoodle signed to Lady Mary to say no more, and everyone was silent. After breakfast, Charles Macdoodle told Lady Mary that it was a tradition in the family that those rumbling carriages on the terrace betokened death. And so it proved, for, two months afterwards the Lady of the mansion died. And Lady Mary, who was a Maid of Honour at Court, often told this story to the old Queen Charlotte; by this token that the old

King always said, ' Eh, eh? What, what? Ghosts, ghosts? No such thing, no such thing! ' And never left off saying so, until he went to bed.

Or, a friend of somebody's whom most of us know, when he was a young man at college, had a particular friend, with whom he made the compact that, if it were possible for the Spirit to return to this earth after its separation from the body, he of the twain who first died, should reappear to the other. In the course of time, this compact was forgotten by our friend; the two young men having progressed in life, and taking diverging paths that were wide asunder. But, one night, many years afterwards, our friend being in the North of England, and staying for the night in an inn, on the Yorkshire Moors, happened to look out of bed; and there, in the moonlight, leaning on a bureau near the window, steadfastly regarding him, saw his old college friend! The appearance being solemnly addressed, replied, in a kind of whisper, but very audibly, ' Do not come near me, I am dead. I am here to redeem my promise. I come from another world, but may not disclose its secrets!' Then, the whole form becoming paler, melted, as it were, into the moonlight, and faded away.

Or, there was the daughter of the first occupier of the picturesque Elizabethan house, so famous in our neighbourhood. You have heard about her? No! Why, *She* went out one summer evening at twilight, when she was a beautiful girl, just seventeen years of age, to gather flowers in the garden; and presently came running, terrified, into the hall to her father, saying, ' Oh, dear father, I have met myself!' He took her in his arms, and told her it was fancy, but she said, ' Oh, no! I met myself in the broad walk, and I was pale and gathering withered flowers, and I turned my head, and held them up!' And, that night, she died; and a picture of her story was begun, though never finished, and they say it is somewhere in the house to this day, with its face to the wall.

Or, the uncle of my brother's wife was riding home on horseback, one mellow evening at sunset, when, in a green lane close to his own house, he saw a man standing before him, in the very centre of a narrow way. ' Why does that man in the cloak stand there!' he thought. ' Does he want me to ride over him?' But the figure never moved. He felt a strange sensation at seeing it so still, but slackened his trot and rode forward. When he was so close to it, as almost to touch it with his stirrup, his horse shied, and the figure glided up the bank, in a curious, unearthly manner—backward, and without seeming to use its feet—and was gone. The uncle of my brother's wife, exclaiming, ' Good Heavens! It's my cousin Harry, from Bombay!' put spurs to his horse, which was suddenly in a profuse sweat, and, wondering at such strange behaviour, dashed round to the front of his house. There, he saw the same figure, just passing in at the long French window of the drawing-room, opening on the ground. He threw his bridle to a servant, and hastened in after it. His sister was sitting there, alone. ' Alice, where's my cousin Harry?' ' Your cousin Harry, John?' ' Yes. From Bombay. I met him in the lane just now, and saw him enter here, this instant.' Not a creature had been seen by anyone; and in that hour and minute, as it afterwards appeared, this cousin died in India.

Or, it was a certain sensible old maiden lady, who died at ninety-nine, and retained her faculties to the last, who really did see the Orphan Boy; a story which has often been incorrectly told, but, of which the real truth is this—because it is, in fact, a story belonging to our family—and she was a connection of our family. When she was about forty years of age, and still an uncommonly fine woman (her lover died young, which was the reason why she never married, though she had many offers), she went to stay at a place in Kent, which her brother, an Indian Merchant, had newly bought.

There was a story that this place had once been held in trust by the guardian of a young boy; who was himself the next heir, and who killed the young boy by harsh and cruel treatment. She knew nothing of that. It has been said that there was a Cage in her bedroom in which the guardian used to put the boy. There was no such thing. There was only a closet. She went to bed, made no alarm whatever in the night, and in the morning said composedly to her maid when she came in, ' Who is the pretty forlorn-looking child who has been peeping out of that closet all night? ' The maid replied by giving a loud scream, and instantly decamping. She was surprised; but she was a woman of remarkable strength of mind, and she dressed herself and went down-stairs, and closeted herself with her brother. ' Now, Walter,' she said, ' I have been disturbed all night by a pretty, forlorn-looking boy, who has been constantly peeping out of that closet in my room, which I can't open. This is some trick.' ' I'm afraid not, Charlotte,' said he, ' for it is the legend of the house. It is the Orphan Boy. What did he do? ' ' He opened the door softly,' said she, ' and peeped out. Sometimes he came a step or two into the room. Then, I called to him, to encourage him, and he shrunk, and shuddered, and crept in again, and shut the door.' ' The closet has no communication, Charlotte,' said her brother, ' with any other part of the house, and it's nailed up.' This was un-deniably true, and it took two carpenters a whole forenoon to get it open for examination. Then, was she satisfied that she had seen the Orphan Boy. But, the terrible and wild part of the story is, that he was also seen by three of her brother's sons, in succession, who all died young. On the occasion of each child being taken ill, he came home in a heat, twelve hours before, and said, Oh, Mamma, he had been playing under a particular oaktree, in a certain meadow, with a strange boy—a pretty forlorn-looking boy, who was very timid and made signs! From fatal experience, the parents came to know that this was the Orphan Boy, and that the course of that child whom he chose for his playmate was surely run.

Legion is the name of the German castles, where we sit up alone to wait for the Spectre—where we are shown into a room, made comparatively cheerful for our reception—where we glance round at the shadows, thrown on the blank walls by the crackling fire—where we feel very lonely when the village inn-keeper and his pretty daughter have retired, after laying down a fresh store of wood upon the hearth, and setting forth on the table such supper-cheer as a cold roast capon, bread, grapes, and a flask of old Rhine wine—where the reverberating doors close on their retreat, one after another, like so many peels of sullen thunder—and where, about the small hours of the night, we come into the knowledge of divers supernatural mysteries. Legion is the name of the haunted German students, in whose society we draw yet nearer to the fire—while the schoolboy in the corner opens his eyes wide and round, and flies off the footstool he has chosen for his seat, when the door accidentally blows open. Vast is the crop of such fruit, shining on our Christmas Tree; in blossom, almost at the very top; ripening all down the boughs!

Among the latter toys and fancies hanging there—as idle often and less pure—be the images once associated with the sweet old Waits, the softened music in the night, ever unalterable! Encircled by the social thoughts of Christmas-time, still let the benignant figure of my childhood stand unchanged! In every cheerful image and suggestion that the season brings, may the bright star that rested above the poor roof, be the star of all the Christian World! A moment's pause, O vanishing tree, of which the lower boughs are dark to me as yet, and let me look once more! I know there are blank spaces on thy branches, where eyes that I have loved have shone and smiled; from which they are departed. But, far above, I see the raiser of the dead girl, and the Widow's son; and God is good! If Age be hiding for me in the unseen portion of thy downward growth, O may I, with a grey head, turn a child's heart to that figure yet, and a child's trustfulness and confidence!

Now, the tree is decorated with bright merriment, and song, and dance, and cheerfulness. And they are welcome. Innocent and welcome be they ever held, beneath the branches of the Christmas Tree, which cast no gloomy shadow! But, as it sinks into the ground, I hear a whisper go through the leaves. 'This, in commemoration of the law of love and kindness, mercy and compassion. This, in remembrance of Me!'

Two Thousand Years of Pantomime

BY BEVERLEY BAXTER

S A DRAMATIC CRITIC I receive two free seats for every new theatrical production in the West End, as well as the smaller theatres in the suburbs. This sounds very agreeable, and indeed it has its pleasurable side, but of necessity a critic sees plays which no sane man would think of doing. Unlike the theatre-going public we are not advised and warned by gentlemen of the Press who admit that they are experts on the drama.

Yet once a year the critic abandons his lofty pose of superiority and becomes not only human but as gullible as any other citizen. It is when Prince Littler invites him to *Mother Goose* or Jack Hylton to *Aladdin* or Tom Arnold to *Cinderella*. Christmas is at hand and the Pantomime Season is about to open.

The critic discovers, to his surprise, that after all he is an intensely popular fellow, his merits being recognised not only by his mature friends but even more by their sons and daughters. As for nephews, nieces and god-children, he is never out of their hearts at this gladsome season. Warmed by this unaccustomed affection and interest the critic gets on the telephone and actually purchases, for ready money, extra tickets in all directions. It is said that the spectacle of a critic purchasing a ticket has caused even the most hard-boiled box office attendant to burst into tears.

Now the strange part about all this is that the critic (and we shall dispose of him altogether in a minute) actually looks forward to seeing the pantomime. ' It's fun to go with the kids,' he says, putting a cigarette back in his case and keeping it for to-morrow. ' They like all this nonsense about dames and brokers' men and wicked sisters.'

' And the principal boy? ' says his wife sweetly.

'Queer thing,' says the critic; 'I often wonder why the principal boy is played by a girl.'

'I can think of two reasons,' says his wife, tartly.

'Probably goes back to the Elizabethans,' declares the critic pompously, 'when girls used to be played by boys. That's why Shakespeare was always dressing his female characters up in boys' clothes because they were more convincing that way than dressed as girls.'

'Rubbish!' says his stupid wife.

But here we shall draw the curtain upon the domestic scene of the critic on the hearth and let him and his wife argue it out. The subject of dramatic critics' wives is one that deserves an article all on its own, and our purpose just now is to discuss pantomimes.

Where did this theatrical extravaganza begin? From whence, as the Good and Beautiful Fairy would say, comes this Yuletide entertainment? Of course the average person would say that pantomime is as English as Brussels sprouts, that it sprang from the soil of England and has never really taken root in any other country.

That answer is nearly accurate except that it is about twenty-three centuries wrong in the matter of origin.

The original pantomimists came to Rome from Etruria in the year 364 B.C. They were called histriones, from hister, a dancer, which accounts for the modern word histrionic which has very little to do with dancing. But in those days the dancers were the only actors, wearing masks and speaking lines.

The Emperor Augustus became the great patron of the art, so much so in fact that he is regarded by some historians (from *histoire*, a tall story) as the inventor of dumb acting. If that is so he has an awful lot to answer for in the modern theatre.

You all know that history repeats itself so it is interesting to note that the *mimes*, that is the dumb actors, became so popular with the knights and the nobles that there was a great deal of fraternisation, and drinking of Roman Highballs at the local Ivy. This made Tiberius very angry so he checked it by prohibiting nobles to frequent the actors' houses or be seen walking with them in the streets, or even climbing the Seven Hills.

Today in London the knights still drink and eat with actors but in the Brigade of Guards an officer has to resign if he so far forgets himself as to marry a dumb actress. Take her to Kew old boy, take her to the

Grand Prix if you've got the francs, but for the honour of the regiment do not, I pray you Horace, take her to the altar.

However, things began to improve for the pantomimists in Rome when Caligula looked on them with favour. You will remember (at any rate you ought to if you don't) that Caligula was so devoted to his favourite horse that he made it a senator. I've often met a senator who proved to be an ass but this was the first time, I am almost certain of my facts, that a horse was made a senator or consul, although I am afraid his vote must have tended to be in the negative.

But again you see history telling the same story twice. Caligula's horse was the authentic origin of the pantomime horse at Christmas, the one with the charming smile and the collapsible back legs—not to be confused with the one you backed in the Derby.

Caligula however, does not deserve as much credit as Nero, who not only played the violin, like Vic Oliver, but also fancied himself as an actor. So he became one of the dumbest stars in the history of pantomimes and was much acclaimed by the critics of his day who did not want to be put on the menu at the Lions' Corner House. Unfortunately Nero's influence was not good. He took the view that since the actors' faces were masked, and as they did not speak, the customers ought to be given something for their money. In other words he was in favour of the human body being revealed since it had to do all the acting.

This may well have been the first discovery of the female leg, although I doubt it. The local Jane Russells also livened up the old mythological tales which were the chosen themes, but I am glad to say that this exhibitionism did not take place without protest. The early Christians were right on the job and said that if this kind of thing continued the Roman Empire would collapse. And so it did, which shows that the critics aren't always wrong.

Yet see how yesterday is the parent of tomorrow, how the womb of night presages the coming of the infant dawn, how history unrolls its carpets throughout the ages, and how tradition is carved from the rough stone of human experience. In fact when you next look upon the noble architecture of the principal boy's legs in pantomime think what you owe to Nero.

It was not until the seventeenth century that the pantomimic act spread to England, but the public did not enthuse as much as the

A PANTOMIME AUDIENCE, BY PHIZ: (I) THE GALLERY

Romans did about the mythological legends. So eventually the popular form was the story of Columbine and Harlequin in which Columbine was a simple village lass and Harlequin, note carefully, was always being chased by comic constables. Thus we begin to see the unfolding of the pattern which has become exclusively British. Instead of being a figure of awe, the policeman is always being worsted by the comics who have the enthusiastic support of the children in the audience in their attempts to evade arrest after breaking the law.

There is in every normal child an instinctive love of the absurd and the incongruous. It demonstrates itself even in the first years of life when a baby will throw dishes from its high chair on to the floor, and gurgle with satisfaction over the deed. The baby knows darned well that this is breaking the law, as well as the dishes, but that only adds zest to the crime. Not only that, it likes to see its father stand on his head, or put on his wife's hat, or fall down the stairs (this always gets a great laugh from the dear little cherub) or crawl under the sofa and bark like a dog.

Deep down in its little mind the infant is making its unconscious protest against the drabness of life in later years, when we all begin slowly to die from a sort of creeping common sense. And here let me say that the wise man, and certainly the happy one, never entirely loses that early love of absurdity. The keener the mind, and the more vivid the imagination, the deeper is the appreciation of the nonsensical. Nothing but a superbly cultivated intellect could have written *Alice in Wonderland* or *The Importance of being Earnest*.

The development of the pantomime was shrewdly based on child psychology. Thus in modern times the rapturous Boxing Day audience finds that the Babes in the Wood are none other than those eminent adults Mr. Nervo and Mr. Knox. Are these two frightened when they are lost in the wood? In a way yes, but they indicate by their jokes that they will be quite all right. Even when they lie down to sleep

(2) THE PIT

32

(3) THE BOXES

Mr. Knox takes care to place a large rat under Mr. Nervo's pillow of leaves, and Mr. Nervo neatly places his shoes on the other Babe's face.

And who is their mother? Bless her heart, it is Monsewer Eddie Grey with his alcoholic nose, his prodigious moustache and his exquisite French phrases. The Monsewer is of course the Dame and when she loses her temper in the kitchen does she send the Babes to bed without supper? Not a bit of it. She hits them over the head with a broom while they pull her skirt off, revealing two such spindly legs that the Monsewer admits he won them from a sparrow on a wager.

But the finer things are not forgotten. There is compulsory education in pantomime as in real life, so off the Babes go to school, where Bud Flanagan (I admit that this is an all-star cast I am assembling) is the schoolmaster who writes on the blackboard:

How Much

Is

Too and Too?

Mr. Nervo says the answer is ' Too Much ' whereupon he and the other Babe give the teacher a spanking. Now to any well regulated child with normal instincts this is exactly how life ought to be. No Adolf Hitler could rise to power in a setting where everything pompous is ridiculed and everything cruel is punished. There is wisdom as well as incongruity in the kingdom of childhood's imagination.

The one pantomime which differs from all the others is *Cinderella* and I wonder that the Labour Government permits it to be shown. In its romantic unfolding it extols class distinction, praises the profit motive, and preaches the lesson that a really nice girl in a lowly position should be careful to marry into the aristocracy where there is a lot of money. It is true that Cinders is fond of Buttons but she does not allow her head to be ruled by her heart. Buttons is her only friend, except of course her poor badgered father, but she has had enough of the kitchen and dreams of better things. Thus she does not even pretend to be coy when the Prince offers his hand after finding her foot. Cinders knew a good thing when she saw it.

Personally I have never been convinced that the size of a maiden's foot was sufficient reason for marriage, but nature in her determination to preserve the continuity of the human race, moves in her own mysterious, inexorable way. It is well known that the daughters of the British aristocracy nearly all have large feet, no doubt due to the amount of exercise they take in their youth. But perhaps for political reasons, the Prince felt that it would be wiser to marry a commoner.

The Americans cannot understand our passion for pantomime. To them it just doesn't make sense, but that of course is its charm. Pantomime doesn't make sense, and if it ever does it will die.

But when you go to one this year think of its long history and its ancient origins, how in its own way it is the human spirit finding relief from the cares and drabness of everyday life. Above all when you laugh at the comedians, give a thought to the great Grimaldi, ' the genuine droll, the grimacing, filching, irresistible clown ' who laboured so hard in bringing laughter to London that he died prematurely, worn out by his exertions.

Sweet ladies and gentlemen, I give you the British Pantomime. Long may it survive to keep the wisdom of childhood alive in all of us.

The Office Party

BY BJ KIDD

In which a formidable Christmas institution is given the deep and detailed study it has long deserved by a (woman) writer whose Christian name must surely be unique—even in the United States.

To AN OLD HAND like myself, the mere sound of the words, The Office Party, conjures up ghosts grinning backward through the years. I see a dignified credit manager taking a curious slow-motion swan-dive down a marble stairway. I see as in a nightmare the escalators of a great department store, crowded with last-minute shoppers, suddenly reverse themselves and proceed slowly backwards. At the top, riding the whirlwind in mad abandon, appears the paper-capped scarecrow figure of Old Snoop, the store's dean of morals. Old Snoop, sniffer after the illicit cocktail, the abbreviated sleeve, the skirt shorter than regulation. I see, in the chill light of a Christmas dawn, the symbolic figure of the assistant advertising manager asleep as peacefully as a baby upon the motherly bosom of a snowbank, his head pillowed on a rocking horse that should have been beneath the stockings a good five hours before. The sobs of crying jags long silenced ring once more in my ears. . . . It is obvious that any one cursed with this kind of recall should seek the services of a competent physician. A total anaesthetic, administered immediately, is the only solution. Then we could wake up the morning afterward with nothing to remind us of the whole grim business but the half-filled highball glass in the bottom desk drawer and the new crop of office feuds, guilt complexes and anxiety neuroses promising to last well into the happy New Year.

But, unfortunately, this practical expedient is not for us. The front office wouldn't like it! You don't want to be a snob, do you? You don't want not to be a good sport? Besides, as a study in anthropology that conveniently telescopes the emerging civilisation of man right back to the Dark Ages in a few fun-filled hours, there is nothing like it! So let you, and you, and you and me brace ourselves and go down, rose-crowned and singing, into the darkness of our own particular mid-winter Walpurgis Night or afternoon.

The main ingredients of The Office Party are as follows:

The tradition. It is probable that the origin of The Office Party is lost in antiquity. This convenient device for showing the staff that the management is all too human and giving the management the tip on what is wrong with Smithers' eyes the mornings he appears in dark glasses when the sun isn't shining cannot have escaped the attention of the Emperors Caligula and Nero. Wasn't it shortly after the *Natalis Invicti Solis* that Petronius sought a razor blade and his bathtub? Queen Elizabeth gave office parties frequently. So did Catherine of Russia. Of course the penalties for indiscreet behaviour were a trifle more severe in those days, though there are still some who sigh for the headsman's axe the morning after. There is no doubt too that all these celebrations were connected with Christmas, which in fact did not exist in the time of the emperors. It was simply a Roman holiday.

The first recorded instance of our truly modern, democratic Office Christmas Party occurs in the scene in which Mr. Fezziwig, bless him, danced so happily with the office char. (' Bloody old fool,' as she remarked graciously later. ' 'Im not 'alf stinkin' and plantin' 'is great boots all over my best nylons. Good show I tripped 'im up, makin' a blinkin' ass of 'imself right there in front of everybody! ')

Today, The Office Party has become A Tool of Management. Such a salubrious occasion for expressing warm human sentiments not customarily found in pay envelopes has not escaped the shrewd intelligences that guide our business destinies. Not for a moment! Should some communist reformer, like your historian, humbly suggest that the staff each be handed the 15s. per which is the customary sum lavished upon this entertainment by looking-forward business, along with a chaste kiss upon the forehead and permission to depart in peace quite early in the day—well, such a crackpot, visionary scene is sure to meet with the scorn it deserves!

The boss. In contrast to management, which is sometimes present in spirit only, the boss is an essential participant. 'We wouldn't enjoy a minute of it if you weren't here, dear Mr. Tompkins.' It is unfortunate that just at this time the boss is generally in the throes of his annual pre-Christmas fantods. His wife's relatives are coming, he hasn't done his Christmas shopping and she wants a Cartier watch and not an eight-guinea black lace nightgown like the one he had such fun buying her last year. Also, the business looks like cracking up, due to all the extra-curricular activities connected with this party.

The boss, bless him, is the Man Who Hates Christmas. We can't blame him. And we know that at the last minute he will come through nobly. But unfortunately this chronic pre-Christmas bearishness often leads him to encourage festivities which he above all should realise are utterly impractical. We shall outline a few of these . . .

The pious party. Beguiled by Weltschmerz and apprehension, the committee may persuade the boss that the excesses of previous years are completely unnecessary. What is needed is a return to the True Spirit of Christmas. Carols, hot cocoa and turkey sandwiches around the piano. The trouble is that it invariably leads to the practice of secret vice —the worst kind, as any psychiatrist will tell you! It leads to the merry smash of smuggled bottles in the elevators, to tell-tale rings on desks and correspondence—to the small, stiff form of the meekest little secretary being carried out to a taxi, feet first. The sudden, brazenly counterpoint interpolation of *Pistol Packin' Mama* from the back row is apt to occur at any moment, much to the disgust of the conformists who are dutifully murdering *O Little Town of Bethlehem* up close where the boss can see them. This precipitates a general and sometimes bloody rebellion on the part of the free spirits, and a feud that will turn any office into an armed camp of the border clans for months. Whether you did, or whether you didn't, you are sure to be hated for ever after by at least half of your fellow workers.

37

The formal dinner is the next most popular choice with an apple-polishing committee. They shrewdly figure that by spending five shillings a plate and allowing two cocktails each, there will be enough for a 1s. 6d. gift all round—' just a gag, of course, nothing serious '—and something really nice for the Best of Bosses!

When the great occasion comes, that worthy, surveying the mournful faces of such of his fellow-workers as have not frankly joined the ranks of the unregenerate in the nearest bar, is attacked by guilty conscience. He has heard rumours that the kids are giving him something handsome—trust the Committee for that—and the cocktail situation is looking a trifle grim. As a result, when the first course is borne in, congealed and forty-five minutes late, simultaneously bountiful pitchers of warm Manhattans and Martinis arrive and begin to flow. Let us draw a curtain over the shambles of the formal dinner. By the time Santa arrives with the presents and the cute jingles the Committee wrote, even the boss can't tell his de luxe self-oiling pen set (the gift for Men of Vision) from the hole he burned in the hotel tablecloth!

The show-off party starts out to be a kind of department miracle play or to impress Management with the talent and ingenuity lurking unsung (and you bet unrewarded) in the Shipping Room or maybe the Newspaper Files. It entails dressing up. It is usually instigated, with paternal pride, by the boss himself, who should know better. The word for how all this turns out is *lousy.* Management, inwardly chafing because, to attend, it has had to omit the opening rounds of the Orpheus Club frolic, is impressed only by its own blindness in allowing Tompkins to embezzle his payroll all these years while he had this troupe of zombies and trained apes doing the work. The zombies and apes, feeling like monkeys in their fine regalia, are equally critical of the Management. Growls and mutters of the coming revolution add a desperate note to the proceedings; Management retires privately resolving that *it hasn't got this labour problem really solved yet!*

The field trip. Occasionally a restless committee, feeling that things must be different this year, thinks to solve the problem by getting away from it all. This, for obvious reasons, is never a hard idea to sell to the higher-ups. But beware! Against you, you will have the very Elements. If, for example, you plan a sleigh ride (God forbid), they will have had to send out the watering trucks to lay the dust on the highways. But if you plan to make wassail in Ye Quainte Olde Inn on the Post

Road, watch for a blizzard. Take it from One Who Has Been There, they'll be digging your fellow workers out of drifts for days ahead. And you will be doing their work. . . .

Well, then, you inquire, what other kinds of Office Parties are there? Of course, there's the kind you and I probably will be attending this year, having learned to avoid all other kinds—the common, garden, semi-impromptu party. It bubbles up out of sheer goodwill. Add ten grains of precaution and one mm. of anxiety and you'll probably be all right. Just be prepared for the usual cast of characters, and I do mean characters. For example: *the bonus marchers.* The bonus is the true Ghost of Christmas Present. Unseen but all-pervasive, like Miss Hickenbustle's new perfume, it haunts the party, jogging the elbows of the guests.

If the bonus handout predates the party, the ninety-and-nine who overestimated their take are already morosely drowning their sorrows. If it does not they are still drowning their sorrows. How do they know they won't overestimate it? The one sure thing is that the bland, pink, unworried faces of the exceptions to the common misery are going to attract most unfavourable attention. In fact the psycho-cultural undercurrent of every Office Christmas Party is surely the determined and alcholic effect on the part of the self-assumed have-nots to gang up on the haves and worm out of them: How Much? When? and How'd *you* Rate It, You Big So-and-So? This usually leads to what we may kindly call Consequences. For instance: *The insulted.* This cast of characters includes you and you and me. In fact it includes everybody. For never was a Christmas party so dead that it failed to produce at least one nasty crack per head.

Sometimes the bon mot takes the form of the challenge direct and results in An Incident. In that case the squared circle should be hastily mobbed by well-meaning bystanders looking for a little action, and the corpse with its black eye removed as quickly and quietly as possible. (You will find it has quite an exhilarating effect on the rest of the party.) But this does not take the place of the *rankling* insult, which is sure to happen to you before the occasion's over. Everybody is making so much noise you may not recognise it at the time. But at 4.30 a.m. you will start from your couch, providing you have sought it by then, with every syllable ringing bell-like in the darkness.

Did that heel *really* say ' *I've been wading through your book all winter* '? Why didn't you paste him one, or at least crack right back, ' *I hope your head is comfortable in those hip boots you're wearing!* '

This is known as delayed reaction. It produces a frustrated Aggression Impulse which isn't good for a blood pressure already overcharged by celebration, or for the future chances for a beautiful friendship between insulter and insultee.

The mysterious stranger. At every party there suddenly appears a mysterious little man. He is usually about five feet six and slightly bald. He looks vaguely familiar but nobody can place him. Somebody thinks he is one of the directors. Somebody thinks he may be a client from Manchester. Somebody else thinks he is the man who runs the elevator. Or somebody who has wandered in from the Pretzel Twisters party next door. Of course it turns out he is the man in charge of records and has been working right in the next office to you for ever. This is called seeing your fellow workers through the eyes of society. They don't show much of their usual wistful charm, do they? In fact there is a whole group we can wrap up and label . . .

The pests. These include the apple-polisher who insists on talking business loudly so the boss can hear him. And the ordinarily repressed drunk who suddenly buttonholes the president and tells him just what's wrong with how he runs the place. (Won't *he* be sorry tomorrow!) And the drunk who wants to sing—but not the song *you* want to sing. And the drunk who does card tricks. There is the *purist* who won't take a drink but labours under the necessity of proving himself a good sport anyway by telling dirty stories. (You want to watch this fellow in dark corners, too, girls.) There is the girl you never could stand and the sudden friendship you form with her, and the embarrassing revelations she makes in the Powder Room and the equally ditto you find you've made to her. Then there are *the wives*. And heaven knows they deserve a separate heading!

There is an excellent bit of protocol for givers of office parties to remember. *All* wives gum the game. (Also husbands.) Let us not share our misfortunes with our innocent next of kin. Let us not by all means, for their innocence will prove unequal to the test. All imported wives arrive at the office party in a state of high suspicion—

and as their suspicions are usually justified, they are apt to depart either in tears or a grand choler, depending on their temperaments. For example, there is the wife who always gets insulted so her husband must fight the office heavyweight to save her virtue. And the wife who has one drink and gives all the embarrassed bystanders within earshot a lecture on her husband's most intimate failings. And the wife who spends all evening long on the trail of a suspected office romance.

With only a passing reference to who pays the cheque and what develops in the aftermath parties that go on and on (for they are not our business; this is only about the Office Party), let us turn bravely to face the worst feature of all our yuletide masochism. It is, all will agree, *the morning after*. The etiquette of this occasion could have a tidy little volume

devoted to itself. The initial problem is, of course, *shall you go in at all*? If you don't, everyone will suspect the worst. If you do, it may well be confirmed. There is no good answer to this one; we leave it to your own aching head. The chances are, you'll sneak wretchedly in, quite tardy, hating yourself and your fellow workers and wassailers with a deep neurotic hatred. That's all right—it will wear off—and meanwhile they are reciprocating heartily. The first hours are worst, for they are spent in mental solitude. Nobody dares to mention the party. Grim and shaken as the survivors of some great calamity, the staff moves zombielike through the routine, confining their pale-lipped remarks to business-like monosyllables. The air is heavy with unspoken questions—What did I do? Who broke the borrowed radiogram? Did the boss go home before I . . .? About eleven o'clock some brave soul ventures a remark, and the ice is broken. Soon all of you are buzzing happily, working off the annual hangover of scandal, blood feuds, hurt feelings and guilty consciences.

41

A
Christmas
Meditation

BY THE DEAN OF ST. PAUL'S

THERE IS A PARADOX, which almost becomes a contradiction, in the Christmas message. We are invited, as it were, to be in two quite different moods at the same time. On the one hand, we are taken back as by no other festival to the simplicities of life. Our imagination moves among the shepherds, the Child and the Mother, the rustic people and their unsophisticated thoughts and feelings. 'Unto us a child is born '—the words evoke the elemental joy and wonder at new life and the ever-renewed existence of that oldest of all human associations—the family. The time for criticisms and sober judgement, we feel, is not now. For a while even the historian or the philosopher draws down the blind, and in the firelight abandons himself to the sweet enchantment of the carols and can believe for a day in fairyland. It is the feast of children and of those who have not lost the capacity to become, now and then, like little children. All this is rightly part of our Christmas celebration. I like to think of those two grave and learned old scholars of Oxford who, being bachelors, used to eat their Christmas dinner together and then pulled crackers and decorated their venerable heads with paper caps. A poor substitute perhaps for the Christmas party where youth sets the pace, but they were doing what they could to claim their share in the communion of the innocents. The pity is that commercialism has invaded the Christmas festival and has tried to exploit the children's feast, extracting dividends from joy that should be spontaneous and simple, but so long as the family exists this human aspect of Christmas will not be wholly spoiled. 'Unto us a child is born'—the cry pierces to depths of our nature which were there before men thought of money or profit and will outlast the Bank of England.

But on the other hand, the Christmas festival invites us to the most profound reflection. There is no other day in the Christian year which opens out such vistas of thought. The passages of Scripture which are read embody the two contrasting moods. We hear the lovely idyll of the Birth as narrated by St. Luke, with its songs of praise, so direct and fresh that they seem to come from the morning of the world, but the Christmas Gospel is not taken from those chapters. The passage which the Church invites us above all to reflect upon is the most philosophical, even metaphysical, in the whole Bible—the majestic prelude to St. John's Gospel. There we do not hear of shepherds, or angels, or even of the Mother. We are taken beyond time, to the roots of existence. ' In the beginning was the Word, and the Word was with God and the Word was God ' . . . passing on to the tremendous climax, ' and the Word was made flesh and dwelt among us (and we beheld his glory, the glory as of the only begotten of the Father), full of grace and truth '. There is the paradox of Christmas, which is really no paradox, if we believe in the Incarnation. The joy which we have in the human life of family and friends and expanding life is not rootless, or a feverish and momentary forgetfulness of the grim facts of existence, it is based upon a belief about the nature of the world, or rather we should say upon a philosophical affirmation and the assertion of a fact in history.

Here then we have the subject of our meditation provided for us: ' In the beginning was the Word ' and, ' the Word was made flesh '. Every phrase of this passage has been commented upon and expounded throughout the Christian centuries. Perhaps the meaning has been overlaid by the comment. We can at least try to look at the words again for ourselves. I think it is a misfortune that our English Bible translates the word ' Logos ' by ' word '. Not that the translation is wrong, but that it is so woefully inadequate. ' Logos ' does mean word, but it also means ' thought ' or ' reason ', and no doubt this is intended by the writer of the Gospel. Scholars have disputed whether the ideas of this prologue to St. John are to be traced to Hebrew or Greek sources, but the question does not seriously affect the meaning, for it makes little difference if the author has in mind the Wisdom, which, according to the Hebrew Scripture, was with God at the creation, or if he is directly inspired by the philosophy of Plato, or of the Stoics. It is more important to observe that the phrase ' in the beginning ' (*in principio*, ἐν ἀρχῇ) does not refer to time. We are thinking here of the ground and principle of all existence.

' In the beginning was the thought.' Goethe held that it would be better to say ' in the beginning was the act ' and many modern thinkers, in their various ways, agree with him. But would it be necessarily good news to hear that, at the centre of all being, was an act? Acts may be senseless, or random, and unless directed and informed by thought, they must be so. It would, however, be good news to be assured that at the centre was thought or reason, for that implies meaning. Thought is a system of meanings and every thought is a meaning. When we can say ' in the beginning was meaning ' we have made an affirmation which has unlimited consequences, both intellectual and practical. There is a strange notion abroad, not always unsupported by Christians, that Christianity is, in principle, irrational. No doubt, some of the doctrines believed by some Christians have been irrational, but no one who accepts the Gospel of John as inspired Scripture could hold that Christianity is not rational in intention. ' In the beginning was the thought '—that might be taken as the charter of all constructive thinking about the world, of all philosophy and science. Does not every enquiry take for granted that the facts do make sense, if we can only penetrate to their inner connections—that mind may be baffled indeed because of the complexity of the material, but never because the material is without rational structure? We might truly say that every research begins with an act of faith which is akin to the opening of the Christmas Gospel—'in the beginning was the Logos'.

We have said 'an act of faith', and so it must be, because we can never prove that the universe is rational, though our thought is rendered sterile unless we assume that it is, and when we do make the assumption, unlimited vistas of understanding open before us. In the frenzy of the French Revolution some fanatics inaugurated the 'Feast of Reason' and set up a harlot to represent the Goddess of Reason in their blasphemous rites. Perhaps it was as much the fault of the Church of their day as their own that they did not know there was already a Feast of Reason—Christmas Day with its message, 'in the beginning was the thought'.

Is this good news only for philosophers? On the contrary, it has the most vital import for the individual who has to live a largely 'unexamined' life. Most observers who have good opportunity of judging agree that the number of persons who are deeply unhappy seems very large—probably greater than in previous generations. The cause of this malaise is often said to be 'mal-adjustment', which appears to be about as sensible as saying that a man died of heart-failure. Of course all unhappiness is mal-adjustment; the really important question is—to what? Doubtless we have a part of the answer when we say, to the society, but only a part. Do we not know men and women who are quite able to cope with all the demands of the environment and carry on smoothly and successfully, but still are deeply unhappy? They are adjusted to society, but not to the universe, or to reality, and the root of their unrest is their suspicion that existence itself is meaningless. Much in our experience goes to support the terrible suspicion. We have felt ourselves hurried along to disaster by forces over which we had no control and which seemed quite irrational. We have survived the war, but we can discern no pattern of a more reasonable world emerging. How plausible to conclude that there is no meaning, and how deadly! The Christmas Gospel in its first words counters this subtle and enervating poison. There is meaning in the world. Though we cannot perceive in detail the working out of the eternal Thought, it pervades all things and all events. It has a place and a purpose for me which no other than I can fulfil, and I may have sufficient insight to know at least that my labour and striving is not vain; it may be a strand in the vast web that the Spirit is weaving on the loom of time.

' The Logos was made flesh.' Here we come to the really distinctive note of the Christian gospel. St. Augustine tells us that he was taught the truth of the Logos who was in the beginning by the Platonist philosophers, of whom he always speaks with respect, but that the Logos was made flesh, ' that he found not in them '. And indeed he could not have found this idea in any philosophy, for it is not a truth which could be excogitated by reason. It is a fact in the realm of events. The prologue to St. John's Gospel, which began with the loftiest principle of being, now, by an abrupt transition, makes an historical assertion. It is useless to minimise the significance, or the challenge of this utterance. Nothing less is claimed than that the eternal divine Wisdom or thought appeared among men—' lived as a citizen among us ', as one of the early creeds has it—in the person of Jesus of Nazareth who was born in Bethlehem, spoke certain words and was crucified about the year 30 just outside Jerusalem. Yet I do not think the writer of this prologue intends that we should imagine the coming of the divine Wisdom to be a sudden irruption without any relation to what preceded, for he seems to imply that the Logos had been in the world before the Only Begotten came ' in the fullness of time '; he seems to imply even that no human soul is devoid of some spark from the eternal Light. ' There was the true light which lighteth every man, coming into the world.' In our modern terms we might paraphrase by saying that human personality was always the sphere where divine wisdom was most plainly manifest—the true Shekinah—and the complete manifestation, so far as we are concerned, must be in a perfect person. For this reason our inspired author can say, ' He came to his own '. It was not into a people alien by nature that the Logos came, like one from a far country speaking an unintelligible language, but to those who were by nature akin, whose life depended on the eternal Wisdom and who could understand its utterance, if they would listen.

No one could deny that all this raises the most far-reaching questions, which have been debated for centuries and probably will be debated so long as men are capable of reasoning. To accept this vision, or interpretation, of the world will always involve an act of faith—a decision which goes beyond the certain conclusions of critical thought. Being a practical decision which determines action, it cannot be based on certainty of the mathematical kind. Anyone who waited for a perfect demonstration of her existence would never kiss his wife. But could anyone doubt that the message of the opening lines of St. John's Gospel, if true, is good news? Surely not. If we can receive it, we have the assurance, not only that the world and our lives have meaning, but that we have the clue to that meaning. The true values of life have been shown to us, not in abstract terms, but in the concrete picture of a human personality and career. There will still be many perplexities; we shall often wonder what our next step ought to be, and still more often find ourselves too weak, or too divided in mind, to take it when we know it, but we shall not be in doubt concerning the direction in which we should go, we shall be in possession of a touchstone by which we can test alleged progress in ourselves, or in our society.

The Logos, says our author, is the true life and the true light of the world; not that there was no life or light before the birth at Bethlehem, but that the partial lights are seen in their real proportions now as they could not be until the ' light shined in the face of Jesus Christ '. I am reminded of a sight which I often had from St. Paul's during the war. It is night, and there are enemy planes about. As I look towards the north, I see many little pencils of light probing the darkness; they come and go, as it appears without plan, and they are very feeble. I wonder whether there is any directing intelligence behind the defence. Suddenly a great searchlight on Hampstead Heath leaps into the sky, like one concentrated ray of the sun, and my mind is reassured. The master light shows me that there is a pattern and a purpose in the defence, for though I cannot tell precisely how the other lights fit unto the strategy, I know that they are not haphazard and isolated. In some such way, perhaps, we might think of Christ the Master Light. He does not abolish the other lights which have illuminated men's path, rather he enables us to understand better what they showed and how they stand with respect to one another, for now we are in possession of the centre of the pattern.

We have one more note to add before our meditation can be concluded—the note of rejection. ' He came unto his own, and his own received him not.'

The suggestion of tragedy is not absent from the story of the Birth —the Child is pursued by those who would destroy Him from the beginning, and the massacre of the Innocents intrudes into the pastoral

47

joy of the shepherds and the Mother. So too, when we are taken by St. John up to the heights of contemplation and interpretation, and shown the universal significance of the event, the element of refusal and frustration comes in. The story and the meaning are not simply happy proclamations of ' God with us '; they tell also of bitter suffering and labour and point onward to that other central mystery—the Cross. To us now they have something to say about our own nature. Those who received him not exercised their gift of freedom and made the choice which was open to them. The divine Wisdom, when He deals with His rational creatures, does not constrain or compel them to adopt the right way. He does not override that liberty to choose life or death which is the condition without which they would be incapable of becoming sons of God. He confronts them with a challenge. There is no festival of the Christian year which has not its own peculiar challenge. The Christmas message is not good news to be accepted passively, but a call to respond. ' To as many as received him he gave power to become sons of God.'

And so we round off our meditation. It begins with a picture, surely the most touching in the world; it goes on to a thought, the most profound and fruitful of all thoughts; but it finishes with a challenge to choose and a call to action, for the Child has a long way to go and we are summoned to follow Him.

Four Nativities

JAN GOSSAERT DE MABUSE (C. 1472–1532), Flemish School.

GENTILE BELLINI (1429–1507), Italian School.

COLOURED WOODCUT (early nineteenth century), English folk-art.

GEERTGEN TOT SINT JANS (c. 1465–1493), Dutch School.

Still Life:
Box and Bottle

BY OSBERT SITWELL

1

IFE IS breaking into new designs, burning, blazing, cooling down, crystallising into new patterns before our eyes, the eyes of a generation dazzled by megalomaniac conceptions and inflamed by virulent dreams. Therefore let us for a moment keep our sight level, rather than fix it upon the heights or depths, and engage our attention with trifles, for, though we cannot rearrange the constellations, it is at least possible for an artist to prevent for a while the memory of some small object to which he is attached from fading out of recollection, and a single tear-bottle from the tomb of Nefertiti tells the poet more about Ancient Egypt than could all the treatises ever written, though their facts were marshalled with consummate skill.

Already, before the second war had come to bring us those innumerable spiritual blessings of which bishops love to speak, many little things of common use were growing rare or had become extinct. To take at random three things that we knew as children, sugar-loaves, fireworks, tangerines done up in silver paper, all these have disappeared, some, it may be only temporarily, some, no doubt, for ever (even today it is necessary to explain to several readers what a sugar-loaf looked like: a smooth, glistening cone, a foot or more high, of moulded sugar). Yet many of these articles had charm, or were agreeable to the touch.

There were, for example, the boxes of Elvas plums that when I was a small boy, graced at Christmas every prosperous table. They have gone. Nevertheless, in those generous and ample days they used every year to be sent to the head of a household by the grocer with whom he dealt (now, on the other hand, it is more probable that he would be obliged to send a present to the grocer). They could be seen, too, piled up in cylindrical towers upon the crowded counters of that season, each story consisting of a drum of coloured paper, or, to be more accurate, of white paper flecked all over with drifts of pink and green. When the lid, invariably with some difficulty, was at last raised off one of the boxes, it revealed the wrinkled plums lying there, sticky, sepia-gold in tone, round, though flattened at the top and sides by the pressure of the box, while, between the fruits in the first layer, separating them, were little spangled darts of tinsel paper possessing an Iberian grace that at once, better than any trademark, proclaimed Spain or Portugal as their place of origin, and themselves as related to those darts, with coloured paper twisted round their handles, with which the *banderillero,* at a certain stage in a bull-fight, pricks and goads his antagonist. . . . Or again, there were to be obtained, at a special tobacconist's in St. James's Street, the china boxes in which Balkan Sobranie cigarettes used at one time to be packed. Square cut, but thin, their rectangular forms showed a degree of elegance in their shape and presentation, and their flat lids, which always lifted off with a slight but characteristic clatter, bore, depicted upon their white, shiny surface, groups of peasants, whiskered men in white ballet skirts, and veiled women in plus-fours.

These boxes, I think, had gone some time before the war, leaving behind them only a meaner progeny in tin and paper; though other things have vanished but lately. Nor is it they alone that have departed; the very shops from which we bought those articles that seem to us to have been in some slight way representative of the old world, shops that typified the spirit of an older London, have also, many of them, disappeared. Where, for instance, is the ' *Chymist* ' we used to see thus placarded in early-nineteenth-century lettering above a chemist's shop off Belgrave Square, and where—and this is the modest announcement of one of the two main themes out of which my composition must be built—where can we buy ' *Segars* ' today (cigars are rare enough)? . . . On the other hand, Mr. Pollock's shop—its business, it is true, now transacted by his daughter, in the same way that he carried it on after the death of his father-in-law—still survives. But then it stands in how different a quarter of the town from that wherein the rich dealt with *chymists* or purchased their *segars;* albeit one that none the less exhaled a certain rather forlorn glamour—Hoxton Street, in fact.

When, nearly a century ago, Mrs. Lane presided at the Britannia Theatre, almost directly across the road from Pollock's, Hoxton had long constituted a centre of English theatrical life repository of the great pantomime tradition. It was essentially the sort of theatre in which Miss Petowker ' of the Royal Theatre, Drury Lane ' must, in reality, have played when in London, and not on tour in the provinces. The late Stanley Lupino, in his excellent autobiography,[1] relates a story told him by Clarkson, the famous whiskered wig-maker and costumier, which exactly renders this atmosphere. One night when the great Sarah Lane was at the height of her renown, young Clarkson had been told to deliver a bundle of wigs below the stage. In an effort to save time, he paid off his hansom opposite the main entrance, and tried to take a short cut through it, still carrying his precious load. He found himself, however, wedged for a whole hour in a solid block of people, for another hour in a crowd slowly moving forward, and, still unable to escape, was finally rushed headlong with everyone else up to the gallery. Nearly suffocated, and partly crushed by a beam, he could only deliver his parcel by persuading a soldier in front of him to heave it on the stage just as the curtain was going up. . . . Mrs. Lane herself was a member of the great Lupino clan, which, since the founders of it first appeared from Italy in the reign of James I and introduced Punch-and-Judy shows to London audiences, has given innumerable artists, clowns, jugglers, dancers, tumblers, acrobats, to the English stage. Of this former period of glory, then, the shop of which I write is the sole residuary legatee. Here was—and is, albeit Mr. Pollock, alas, himself has gone—a place entirely unlike any other, and belonging in its essence to London, to the London of the harlequinade.[2]

In early life, Mr. Pollock had been for a time a clown. It is said that all men retain about them until their end signs of their first profession, and it was noticeable that his hair fell naturally into the three *poufs* that are part of the mask of his original calling. Behind him, as he used to stand at the counter, were innumerable pigeon-holes, like those we saw formerly in the shops of old-fashioned hosiers, who would turn

---

[1] *From the Stocks to the Stars: An Unconventional Autobiography*, by Stanley Lupino. Hutchinson and Co., 1934.

[2] But scarcely a few months after Sir Osbert Sitwell wrote this essay (1943), Miss Louisa Pollock's shop was severely damaged by bombs and forced to close down. A company formed by Mr. Alan Keen and Sir Ralph Richardson has since acquired her stock and plates.

PENNY PLAIN BACKGROUND, SCENE 4, *Timour the Tartar* (1849)

round to draw out of them dusty paper packets, carefully done up with string, of socks and gloves; packets that would inevitably take some time to undo and thus increase the pleasurable expectation of the prospective buyer. In this case, however, the compartments contained prints, a penny plain, and twopence coloured—and, indeed, the extra penny demanded was a cheap price to pay for such an expenditure of vivid primary colours. Some of the designs were by George Cruikshank, and by other known artists of his day, but the majority were drawn by the bearers of unfamiliar names, and consisted of theatrical scenes of long ago, and portraits of the great popular stars who had performed in them. These last were iconic and conventional; crinolined beauties, formal in gesture, with large, open eyes in Byzantine faces, and with eyelashes, each of them delineated separately, and long as those of a film-star today. The very names of the dramas in which they acted summon up a lost world, often exotic, but, for the most part, to be seen round us every winter. On the whole, in the background of these scenes, snow and frost prevail; trees, their branches weighed down with tinsel snow, reveal their black bareness against a blue, polar sky. And we wonder where we can find a southern counterpart to this world, which is another, though humourless variation of that portrayed by Breughel the Elder, only belonging to the early nineteenth century, instead of the mid sixteenth; a world which the starving actors of that time knew only too well, as they trudged or bumped along through the glittering white landscapes, their noses blue, their feet just tingling with life, their minds full of the next town, over the hill, and what fortune it would bring them.

These stylised and glowing scenes then, from *Timour the Tartar* or *The Brigand*, though in themselves they seem to belong to so fabulous a past, can still be purchased: whereas cigar-boxes, albeit the warm visions depicted within them provide to those prints the dulcet southern counterpart for which we have been searching, are much more difficult to come by. . . . Let us, therefore, take down an old and empty box, lying on a shelf, and study it, for, in the essay that follows this introduction, I shall strive to paint for the reader another kind of still life, consisting of a box and bottle, and a twist of coloured paper. The bottle, empty like the box, is of stoneware, a tall cylindrical shape, except for its drooping shoulders, with a small handle attached to its

PENNY PLAIN BACKGROUND, SCENE 2, *The Brigand* (1836)

spout, and a heavy, old-fashioned seal, carved on it in relief, two-thirds of the way up its length. Its tone is that of a dove's wings, in light shades of grey and brown. By its side, and a little to the front, is the cigar-box, marked with a name famous in all the money markets of the world. The lid has been thrown back, away from us, and the white, shiny flap lies, as it were, dead, turned inward within the empty box, from which still rises the perfume of cedar and fine tobacco, and thus we can see, in reverse upon this polished whiteness, a picture in strong hues, and, further, in relief, embossed; an example of the only millionaire-folk-art, as we may term it, in existence. The rendering of this highly coloured scene, the way the creases and bulging fold of the paper distort its intention must be as clear, and incisive as that of the embroidered panels that form the stole of the stooping acolyte in El Greco's *Burial of Count Orgaz*. . . . By the side of the box lies a broken cigar-band in scarlet and gold.

These three objects, painted solidly, I hope, show against a background of blues and greens, variable in tone and executed in broad strokes . . . but, as we continue to regard them, we shall notice that, for all their apparent volume and density, they are portrayed in a surrealist manner, and that, through the pale, antiquated form of the stone jug, we begin to perceive, not only the groves of orange trees which might, perhaps, have been suggested merely by the still pervasive aroma of this *curaçao* bottle, but also the broad features, splayed in darkness, of negroes and negresses, and the image of an island, floating light and bubble-like between the tropic sky and tropic sea; through the broken paper ring, the figure of a Cuban dandy of a hundred years ago; while, beneath the lines of the cigar-box, is to be traced the shape of the island in which he lived, of Indians crowned with feathers, smoking in their accustomed silence, of trees that blossom superbly in vermilion and azure and amethyst under a hot sun tempered by cool breezes, of waters that cover with their sheets of glass oceanic gardens, and, in short, of a life of an intensity that never dies down, flares day and night save when it smoulders through the noon. . . . But, above all, these groups and vistas which appear, when we look more closely, to break through the surface of the picture, make us feel the presence of a strong and alien sun that is touching the skin round the corners of the eyes and soaking through our thin silk shirts.

2

Though the pipe had been the favourite method of consuming tobacco among the American Indians, cigars, or at least a form of primitive cigar, had been smoked there long before the advent of Columbus. Cuba soon became the chief place for the growing of the fine tobacco leaves required for cigars, its climate being particularly favourable for their cultivation. The best leaves of all were formerly reserved for the personal use of the King of Spain. And Spain was the European country in which the smoking of cigars first became popular, playing an important part in the life of the poorer as well as of the richer classes. It long remained, however, a purely Spanish idiosyncrasy, and it was not, indeed, until about the time of the French Revolution that the fashion invaded most of Europe, reaching France and Austria in 1796 from Hamburg. There are reasons, however, for thinking the habit of smoking cigars spread to England from Spain when the veterans of the Peninsular War returned home. Fairholt[1] tells us that in 1823 only 26 lb. of manufactured cigars were imported into England, but that the duty being then reduced, the next year showed a return of 15,380 lb., rising in 1830 to 253,882 lb.!

Fairholt has much to say of accessories of smoking; especially does he denounce ornamental cigar-cases. ' When men,' he writes, ' enshrine cigars in pearl cases, elaborated with metal work, that make them seem only fitted for the scent cases of a lady's boudoir, they may be looked upon with due contempt, not only by ladies, but by those of their own sex who adhere to the honest, useful case of plain Russian leather.' Yet he makes no mention either of cigar-bands or of cigar-labels, though one might have imagined that the pictures on these, inspired by the soft south, would have roused him to similar flights. For, in spite of their being, as we have noted, possessed of a peculiar kind of accuracy of observation—being, in fact, more true to Cuban nature than truth itself—it must nevertheless be admitted that the actual scenes depicted are not those with which we meet every day, even in this fantastic island. Let us look at the Larranaga label in front of us, by the side of the grey bottle.

[1] *Tobacco: Its History and Associations*, by F. W. Fairholt, F.S.A. (with 100 illustrations by the author), was published apparently ten years after the author's death, by Chatto & Windus, London, 1876.

There it lies, with a bulging fold in it. . . . It is, I should judge by the light, the early morning; a dewy, rather smudgy freshness prevails, lightly swathing the haze of green vegetation, the thin, spider-leaved palm trees and, even, the blue sky, which holds in it the promise —as yet only the promise—of a burning day. Out of this background towers a forceful, Palma-Vecchio-like blonde, clad in a white robe, and wearing a debutante's tuft of feathers, only that these are dyed in crimson and Cambridge-blue. In one hand she clasps a trident. She is being borne along towards us in a pony-cart, drawn apparently by two lions, although one of them, no doubt owing to some perspectival trouble of the artist's, has got part of its massive head underneath the scarlet travelling rug which a friend, presumably, has thrown thus heavily over the lady's knees. The noble beasts are being led along, in the style of Derby winners, by various pink, yellow and beige children, crowned or turbaned, and they, I hold, can be identified with some confidence as typifying the four quarters of the globe. The whole conception is lightly spattered with gold, as though the Cuban fire-flies had refused to go home in the morning, and is, further, en-closed in an elliptical ring of gold coins, embossed and standing out from the paper. Indeed, these coins, we note, seem to play a pre-ponderant part in this and every similar design, a miraculous gold manna, falling from blue skies and larger than the heads of lions. . . . Of course, it *is* a little gaudy, that we must admit, and is best seen, perhaps, as the grey smoke from your cigar drifts across your eyes and slightly veils the enchanting scene.

Not only, then, does such a picture possess a strange kind of warm, carnival-like truth, but also the same sort of fascination that appertained to the problem-pictures, formerly so teasing, if unfortunate, a feature of recurrent Royal Academies. . . . Take, for example, another label from the collection—now the truth is out! I have formed a gallery of these delightful labels, that were still, I believe, being produced every day until the war came, continuing to present us with a sense of formalised and stylised beauty to be found existing nowhere, except in Hoxton prints, and much more comforting, too, than those, in that they make us feel both warm and rich. . . . Take, then, another example. . . . Partaga will show you, beneath the rather set hovering of an eagle with spread wings, a crowned Empress, of indeterminate features, proudly seated on her throne and plainly commending two

females draped in Greek robes that might have been invented by Alma-
Tadema save that they are more tropical in hue. One of them carries
a palette, and so must surely be the Muse of Painting, while the other,
a neater and altogether less Bohemian figure, I should say, holds a
wreath of laurel or bay leaves, done up with a white ribbon or even, it
may be, by some flight of allegory altogether beyond me, with a bunch
of white feathers. On either hand, beneath a shower of golden guineas,
mulatto cupids stagger under the weight of cornucopias of pineapples
and serpoté, custard-apples and passion fruit, avocado pears, orchids
and lilies and many flowers of which the varieties are unknown to
us. . . . And here we may pause to observe how luscious, in every
vista, are the flowers and fruit, up to the richest millionaire standards—
the sort of bouquets and baskets in the description of which, upon a
Rougon-Macquart table, Zola would have luxuriated—and yet at the
same time plainly showing the gratitude of the artist to the creator of
this bountiful paradise, who, as in ' the remote Bermudas ',

> . . . does in the pomegranate close
> Jewels more rich than Ormuz shows;
> He makes the figs our mouths to meet
> And throws the melons at our feet.

There appear, also, to be accumulations of objects on either side of
the cupids; trophies of wheels and bronze vases and lyres and, very

distinctly, a yellow bowler hat, and an 1840 clock of incredible Gothic complication and confusion. The whole is set in the primrose light that follows dawn or precedes sunset in these countries, and there are flowing ribbons and, of course, gold coins.

Often, in the background—though not of the two we have examined —are views of sea, volcanic mountains, and of huge sailing ships, argosies with accompanying escorts of flying-fishes. . . . And some of the labels show us street scenes and *plazas*, and at these we must glance, if only because they throw light on the epoch in which they were drawn. They take us to great gilded palaces wherein the cigars are made, huge, sun-splashed *plazas* across which sleek horses, prancing with the very same updrawn action of the hooves as we see in Colleoni's bronze horse in Venice, and driven by coachmen in livery and top-hats, are bearing crinolined ladies, reclining in vehicles as light and elegant as shells. It is a splendid world, indeed, and one in which, it is made plain, every lady, in the phrase of the time, kept her own carriage. Today, however, a few ladies have chosen to issue forth on foot, under the shade of parasols, and various men in frockcoats are bent almost double as, in acknowledgement of a bow, they sweep their hats low, towards the ground. . . . Nevertheless, most of the pictures take us to less sophisticated scenes, to day-dreams of Southern beauties gazing down through eyelashes encrusted with tears as though with diamonds, upon dark young gallants with curling whiskers, gallants who are clad, moreover, in Tudor doublet and hose, repoussé in that fashion of which these artists, these processes alone, seem to hold the secret. The palm trees above them betray a spiky, rather centipede-like quality, and we can almost hear the warm drone and humming of tango, rumba and cubana as they float across the little waves that so often occur in these pictures, and the white perukes of which curl so modishly.

Even the names of the brands seem to possess the same subtle lilt to them, the same chirruping, as we murmur Larranaga, Partaga, Estrella, Integridad, Cabana, Eldorado, Rey del Mundo, Santa Damiana. Surely here beats the same rhythm as in Cuban music, which has, sounding in it, so much of the cicada's vibrant shrilling? Indeed this insect seems with the whirring of its wings to provide the basis for it, in the same manner in which the notes of a thrush afforded, it might be, a foundation for English music of the great age. And we may, moreover, note here, as appropriate, that the *Oxford English*

Dictionary offers the word cicada or cigala as the origin of the word cigar—and indeed some physical likeness exists between them; both show the same cylindrical shape, with diminishing ends, the same dark colour.

There is another point to notice. . . . Just now we mentioned a dark young gallant; on the label, he stands on a golden ladder, clasping in his arms a fair-haired girl, who hangs entranced across a balcony: Romeo and Juliet! And is it not singular that a cigar, so often regarded, in combination with the top-hat, as giving the stamp to, being the very embodiment of, materialism, should so often exhale, in the decorations that set it out, such romantic ideals? Love or poverty, or both, figure in almost every label, as in *Romeo y Julieta* or *Byron*. Political conceptions, too, are plainly idealised, these large classical-looking females shaking hands, these lions and spinning-wheels, all possess a meaning—though sometimes one that is difficult to follow—are, it may be, a Testimonial to International Virtue or something of that sort, or a Tribute to the Supremacy of the Arts, or signify the possible inauguration of a *Pax Cubana*. Again, all the designs abound in flowers and fruit, both of them—except, of course, in the case of Eve's apple—the most innocent of all Nature's creations. . . . We should have presumed, then, after a first glance at these boxes, and without a previous knowledge of the luxuries they extol, that they had been called into being, not for the hard-headed, hook-beaked tribes of magnates, company directors, bankers and speculators, sitting all day long at enormous desks in offices, but for some race of simple, child-like being; a genial, light-hearted sort of creature who knows nothing of practical affairs, and finds—as the Sultan Abdul Hamid, with his unrivalled flair for national psychology, claimed to find, when the British Ambassador interviewed him in order to lodge a protest against the Armenian Atrocities—his ' only interest in birds and flowers '.

None of these pictures, alas, bears a date. It is impossible to pronounce with certainty when they made their appearance, who designed them, or whether any were of recent manufacture. But I believe that the street scenes, and the shower of gold coins which edge the sky in nearly every instance or depend from the trees like great gold fruit, may supply a possible clue to the solving of two of these problems, though not to that of attribution. Upon these coins—awards, it must be assumed, at various international exhibitions—are occasionally to be distinguished, though very often they are too vague in outline to admit of absolute identification, the effigies of the rulers of European States. Never, not once, however, do we see upon them the ferocious eyes and timid moustache of Hitler, the jutting jowl of the Italian tyrant, or the slanting moustachios and jovial, Red-Riding-Hood-like smile of Uncle Joe. . . . No, it is Napoleon III, over and over again, and sometimes the square-bearded Leopold II of Belgium and the Congo, and, in one instance, the whiskered but chinless profile of a strangely young Emperor Franz Josef, his head sycophantically belaurelled. Moreover it is to be noticed that, while many carriages are shown, and there even occurs in one of them a very old-fashioned, high-seated type of tricycle, not a single motor car figures in the street scenes. Further, the old monarchical flag of Spain, floating above the *Fabrica Real*, securely places the epoch in days previous to the Spanish-American War. . . . All these facts, taken in conjunction, must lead us to conclude that the majority of designs were contemporary with the last decade of the Second Empire; a time which also saw the heyday of cigar-smoking in Europe. Fairholt, for example, writing in the same period, enumerates sixty-six kinds of cigars published by one London importer alone in his list. It was an era when every country in Europe possessed a crowned emperor, king or prince, and when revolutions were confined to the boundaries of the Southern and Central American states. It would seem, then, that cigar-smoking accords with peace even better than the pipe—though, on second thoughts, a tabulation of the revolts, wars, and civil wars that have taken place in Cuba itself may lead us to abandon our new theory.

We had better, therefore, stop moralising and turn to consider the broken cigar-band which lies by the side of the box and bottle, and manifests, on a miniature scale, suited to its dimensions, a similar quality to that of the label. The particular example in front of us is somewhat in the shape of a signet ring, and shows a bearded and reflective head contained in a gold and scarlet circle. . . . Yet bands such as this are, for all their splendour, merely vestigial ornaments that conceal a former use, and indicate a history. . . . The Cuban dandy has always indulged in a singular extravagance, almost a frenzy, of dress. During the forties of the last century he affected a style that recalls that of the Mexican bandits who made so perpetual and ever popular an appearance in English musical comedies in the days between the wars, except that his air was neither so ludicrous nor so brutal, being more soft and foppish. The costume consisted of a wide light hat, dark whiskers, ear-rings, a silk shirt of brilliant hue, a huge belt, often with a revolver tucked in it, fawn trousers and a pair of lemon-coloured gloves of which the owner was always peculiarly, and justifiably, proud. . . . Now cigars, in their native habitat, as indeed throughout the New World, are smoked, not in a dry but in a damp, or green, condition, and, since it was the fashion for the dandy to smoke them all the time that he strolled in the *plazas* or through the plantations, they unfortunately left a brown stain upon the fingers of his very exquisite gloves. In consequence it became the practice of such elegants to wrap a twist of ordinary paper round each cigar where they held it, so as to save discoloration—until one day an enterprising member of the Cabana firm, the oldest-established factory in Havana, suddenly comprehended that in a glorification of this paper band lay an ingenious new method at once of pleasing his patrons and advertising his goods. It need scarcely be added that his example, or dodge, if we prefer that word, was followed immediately by every other firm in Havana. . . . Thus of masculine vanity were born these splendid strips of paper, shaped and emblazoned and adorned with a thousand touches of southern fantasy. Moreover it affords a curious footnote to the history of social shibboleths to reflect that although, in the Cuba of a century ago, to smoke a cigar with the band still on it was the height, and indeed added the very stamp, of fashion, yet here in England, for the last fifty years at least, it has been considered the acme of ostentation and bad form.

Now we must return, though, to the larger examples, and, through them, analyse their art, comment upon its affinities . . . first noting in them the singular and utter lack of kinship that they show with Gauguin, the best-known painter of tropical life. But his were naïve scenes, attempted by someone sophisticated, struggling backward by means of colour and feeling; while these are scenes of attempted sophistication executed by a naïve. Everything in the world of the cigar-box label is bright, light and European—suspiciously bright and European. Artistic anti-kink, as it were, has been liberally applied. Moreover, these artists have stretched towards a different ideal, to them romantic, to us banal, since it is seen to have been achieved elsewhere. In spite, then, of the pretensions to luxury and pomp which

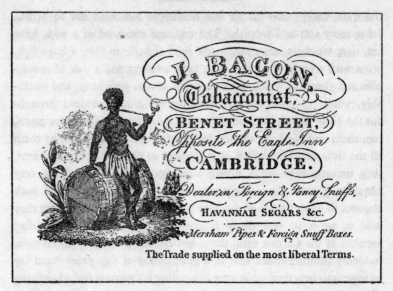

'HAVANNAH SEGARS': TRADE PLATE (ABOUT 1805) FROM MESSRS BACON BROS. OF CAMBRIDGE

these labels exhibit, their essential quality is that of innocence—a blessed innocence sometimes resembling a little that of Blake or Fra Angelico; though very different from their work, it must be admitted, in point of drawing and colour. On the other hand it is also permissible, as we study them, to suggest a still nearer comparison with two men, with the most sophisticated, no less than with the most naïve of modern artists. Notwithstanding the wooden stiffness of the figures, the same voluptuous and now demoded exquisiteness that we observe in the drawings of Aubrey Beardsley—notably in the illustrations to his *Under the Hill*—can be traced in some of them. We find the same serious preoccupation with delicious trifles, though all are nevertheless subordinated to the line, and observe how the birds and butterflies and flowers and fruit bear an identical relationship to the beings they surround. While, in a direction apparently the most opposite, an obvious kinship to Douanier Rousseau makes itself evident. Not, of course, that I am attempting for a moment to insinuate in either case a direct influence, but merely that there existed some similarity in the point of view from which such art sprung.

Thus, just as the Douanier Rousseau could never comprehend how it could be that his extremely unusual and poetical renderings of tigers and Mexican jungles, and of the patriotic celebrations of the Third French Republic, were not chosen for the Salon by the hanging committee, because to him his pictures seemed to touch the height of academic realism, so, I take it, would these unknown artists have been unable to perceive in what respects their creations were unusual or did not conform to drawing-room standards, and how their dreams—to which, perhaps, their share of a darker blood imparted a certain passionate vehemence—of palm and pineapple, and the various carnival figures of Democracy or the Arts, with their whole illusory circumambience of blue sky and golden prizes, differed from the reality. And we cannot help wondering, as we examine the extraordinary scenes they depicted, so entirely unlike the run of the production of other artists of their day—if it be some seventy years ago, as I incline to believe—who these anonymous men were, and whether they essayed any bigger or more important works. . . .

In vain, alas, did I search Havana and its immediate surroundings for fresco or wall-painting by the same hands, notwithstanding that whenever I saw a big building, palace or church, I forced an entry, hoping to find within a vast design of Peace leading her team of lions through a tapestry of rosebuds and hibiscus, while a flying-fish hovered aloft with an olive branch, or even to be confronted with an appropriate historical scene, such as the Landing of Columbus; an episode which graces one cigar-box in my collection, and the delineation of which would perhaps, even on a wall, have been carried out in the same natty and execrable shallow relief. . . . I failed to discover them, or anything that resembled them—but I found, instead, a city more fascinating, withal, than I had imagined it could be, and a country more lovely, much more lovely.

It is pleasant to be able to think still of Havana and of Curaçao. . . . For even the objects that remind us of travel have vanished of late years, and it is for this reason that I have sought to paint my still-life, of the empty bottle, standing there, the open box, the broken band. There they are yet, in front of me, the stoneware bottle, so typically Dutch in its plain, strong solidity, as it catches the light that pours into the room from a wide Derbyshire perspective, hilly, umbrageous, with tufts and plumes of smoke and layers of mist. The light plays upon the curves of the bottle's neck, in cool, broad tones of grey and fawn and almond-husk. It brings out a new watery whiteness in the white of the paper with which the box is lined, and yet also emphasises the threading of gold among the blue and scarlet of the label. . . . As, for a last time, we look at it, the sound of a rumba comes once more stealing over a glassy tide from a coastline that seems to resemble a feather as it lies so lightly on the water. The whole island vibrates to the rhythm, nor will it cease throughout the hot noon or the night; not until, indeed, the electric lights, shining here and there, dwindle down to take second place, as the palest green morning light begins to prosper under the branches of the trees, as if born of them, and to illumine delicately the scarlet and orange trumpets of the flowers among which the people dance. . . . While we listen, to try to catch the precise air that is being played, the sound alters, and, with it, the scene. Now each strand of the feather is a forest tree, a gigantic tree, growing larger and larger. We are in a forest before dusk, at that moment when the great diapason begins, when a shudder passes through the leaves that have lain dead all day, and every insect, for green mile upon green mile, with a rustling and clapping of its wings, with every variety of rustling and clapping and shrilling, gives praise to its creator for the sure prospect of dusk and of the cool that comes with it. That is the music of the tropics, a music which no other region knows.

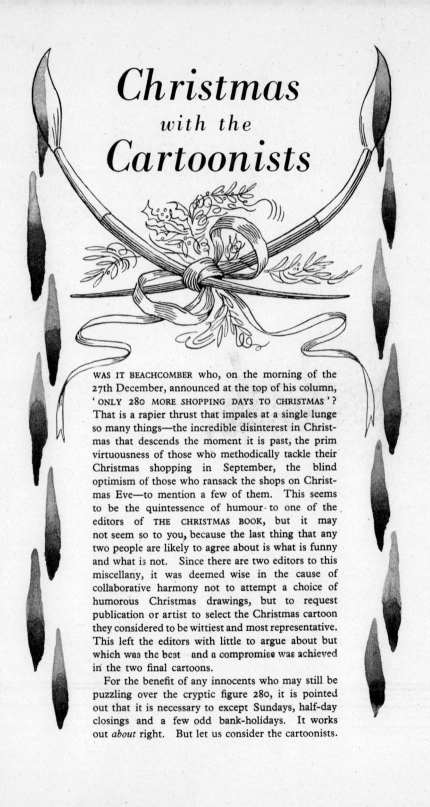

Christmas
with the
Cartoonists

WAS IT BEACHCOMBER who, on the morning of the 27th December, announced at the top of his column, 'ONLY 280 MORE SHOPPING DAYS TO CHRISTMAS'? That is a rapier thrust that impales at a single lunge so many things—the incredible disinterest in Christmas that descends the moment it is past, the prim virtuousness of those who methodically tackle their Christmas shopping in September, the blind optimism of those who ransack the shops on Christmas Eve—to mention a few of them. This seems to be the quintessence of humour · to one of the editors of THE CHRISTMAS BOOK, but it may not seem so to you, because the last thing that any two people are likely to agree about is what is funny and what is not. Since there are two editors to this miscellany, it was deemed wise in the cause of collaborative harmony not to attempt a choice of humorous Christmas drawings, but to request publication or artist to select the Christmas cartoon they considered to be wittiest and most representative. This left the editors with little to argue about but which was the best and a compromise was achieved in the two final cartoons.

For the benefit of any innocents who may still be puzzling over the cryptic figure 280, it is pointed out that it is necessary to except Sundays, half-day closings and a few odd bank-holidays. It works out *about* right. But let us consider the cartoonists.

ROWLAND EMETT
selected by Punch

' Ah, HERE comes the Christmas post ! '

NICOLAS BENTLEY
selected by the artist

Courtesy the New Statesman

Introducing the guest of honour the Mayor explained that the reason Father Christmas had not arrived earlier in the festive season was that the Town Council had inadvertently sent the cesspool emptier to meet him instead of a lorry.—*Wisbech Standard.*

GILES selected by the Sunday Express

'Wait till they get to the bit about " peace on earth and mercy mild "—then let 'em have it.'

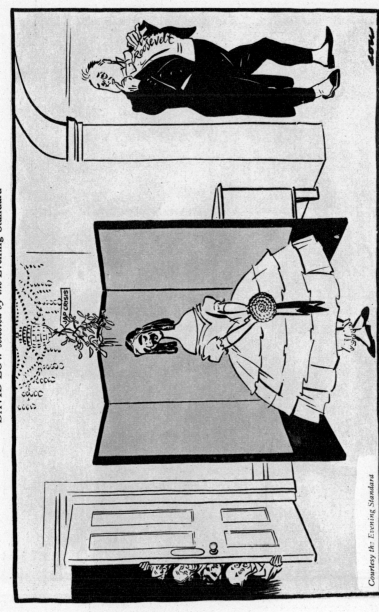

DAVID LOW *selected by the Evening Standard*

A British-American Christmas Card (1937)

OSBERT LANCASTER
selected by the Daily Express

' Brightly shone the moon that night,
Tho' the frost was cruel,
Extra brightly, just to spite
The Minister of Fue-oo-el.'

JAMES THURBER
selected by the spear side of the Christmas Book

' It's Parkins, Sir ; we're 'aving a bit of a time below stairs.'

' My husband is giving me a mink coat for Christmas, and I'm giving
him a muff to match.'

The golden age was
never the present one

Memory is the
treasurer of the mind

Customs are
lost for want of use

Now is now
and Yule's in winter

Christmas Numbers

BY JOHN L. BOTT

For the past thirty years John Bott has been concerned with the production of juvenile publications on the staff of the Amalgamated Press. This means that he is familiar with nine-tenths of the anonymous or pseudonymous creators of the comics, magazines and annuals that diverted us in early youth; since almost all the famous children's periodicals emanate from The Fleetway House, Farringdon Street (familiar habitat of ' Your friend the Editor '). From thence are issued—or, alas! were issued, for many of the old favourites disappeared early in the war and even Billy Bunter has apparently dwindled to a mere comic strip—Chips, Comic Cuts, The Jester, Rainbow, Puck, Tiger Tim's Weekly *and, for those more advanced in years*, Chums, The Magnet, The Gem, The Boy's Friend, The Girl's Friend, Greyfriar's Herald, *the fourpenny ' Library ' series, including* Sexton Blake *and* Nelson Lee, *as well as the* Playbox *and* Holiday Annuals *—to mention only a few! Thus the enormous grey building in E.C.4 with its rabbit warren of stone corridors is the strange cradle of what, to the generations over twenty-five, at least, are the never-to-be-forgotten figures of the Chums of the Remove—the Famous Five—and of course the Terrible Three (St. Jim's) and the Fistical Four (Rookwood) who, in their forty odd years' existence hovered perpetually—as someone, probably Mr. Noel Coward, put it—on the brink of adolescence; of the Cliff House Girls, Barbara Redfern, Marjorie Hazeldene, Bessie Bunter ' and Co '; of the irrepressible Pickles, the Bruin Boys, Weary Willie and Tired Tim, of Bluebell and Val Fox the Detective, who never failed to ' throw his voice ' with unerring accuracy. Who has not, in their time, obediently looked out for ' another long ripping instalment ' or ' next week's Bumper Christmas Issue ' ? A childhood deprived of such simple pleasures would have been as dull as that of Little Lord Fauntleroy—who would, incidentally, have been given short shrift at Greyfriars. Indeed, the situation, as Frank Richards would have dealt with it, is not difficult to visualise : ' Bump! went the Noble Duffer of Greyfriars. "Yarooh! Lemmegerrup!" yelled his lordship . . . ' But this is stealing Mr. Bott's thunder. . . .*

'ear Father Christmas . . .'

Go back, go back through misty memories to the days when you wrote a letter beginning thus. For who has not, in their time, written to Father Christmas? There can be very few whose hand, guided by Mother maybe, have not written to that universal provider of breathless happiness. And he never failed us, for in the thrill of the things that came in answer to that letter we did not notice that the star or the little sister for which we had asked were not in the stocking, so clean and unspotted after its magic journey through the frosty night and down the sooty chimney to the bed's end.

Everything in that stocking, in all the stockings in all the homes, was wonderful . . . just what was wanted. Expected and unexpected, all were Heaven upon Earth.

Looking back, what gifts figured, and still figure, most often in Christmas stockings? The answer is books, children's books, children's Christmas annuals, annuals whose pictures and stories bear re-reading and re-looking at a hundred times in the year. And not only for the year did those pages hold magic, for on through all the years we carry in our minds snatches of verse, humorous pictures and characters whose adventures caught and held our fancy.

With those Annuals there is linked in our memories the Special Christmas Double Numbers of periodicals, the snow thick upon their titles, with holly round the pictures and more often than not a feast of good things to eat as a finish to the adventures in picture and story.

As we think, titles and names come back to us . . . Playbox, Rainbow, Tiger Tim, The Bruin Boys, Val Fox the Ventriloquist Detective, Chips, Weary Willie and Tired Tim, Casey Court, The Red Rovers, Constable Cuddlecook, Tom Merry and Co., Jack, Sam and Pete, Sexton Blake, Harry Wharton, Billy Bunter and Bessie Bunter and a multitude more. There is surely no one person who has never a memory of some character first met in Christmas Numbers or needs but the mention of a name to carry them back through the years?

Your favourite? Was it Professor Radium, the inventor of those astounding gadgets and contrivances that always failed to work in the right way at the right moment? The libretto under each picture had about it a crazy improbable-possibility that has perhaps only been equalled by Beachcomber or Stephen Leacock.

Or was it the Mulberry Flats with its true-to-life variety of tenants ranging from the monied gentleman on the ground floor to the impoverished artist in the attic?

On somewhat similar lines was Racketty Row, a parade of shops in the free and easy pre-control era. There was a florist, butcher, baker and so on to the end, where was situated the Police Station or 'Cop Shop,' complete with prisoner watching the passing show through his cell bars, enlivening the proceedings with apt remarks and, on occasions, escaping in picture one, only to return himself safely to custody before the last picture. Was the Row your favourite?

Perhaps your choice is a younger memory . . . The Pickles, brother and sister, all innocent-eyed and the lucky possessors of Fluff the dog who never failed to have something to say.

There was another dog we can remember, that most mongrel of mongrels, Homeless Hector, whose four legs looked for all the world like four large, long meat bones. And there was Moonlight Moggie, prima donna of the tiles and turner to good account of no matter what was cast at her from up-flung windows.

Other names come crowding back. . . . Waddles the Waiter, still waiting. . . . Bluebell, full of riddles. . . . Rupert the Chick, looking not a day older than when he was first hatched in somebody's mind and many, many others that you will recall.

Surely here, in the provision of popular entertainment for children, is something in which Britain led and still leads the world, for in almost every country you will find among the pages of the magazines British characters reproduced from our papers. For the past fifty years the editors and staffs, the artists and authors, have really known and understood children, their likes and dislikes, their hopes, their longings and their fears.

Their fears! There is much in knowing that. All these well-loved characters have made young people happy, they have held our interest but, unlike the stories of so many other lands, especially those of Middle Europe, they never frightened us. The creators of these characters, the devisers of their adventures could have been no mere theorists in the psychology of children; they are practical men and women who know what children like and see that they get it.

And who are they? In the main a tradition of anonymity holds sway. A long succession of editors and assistants, authors and artists have come and gone serving well their young public, chiefly content to be Uncle Jack, or Uncle Ben or The Editor. No editor publicises his name in the publication for which he is responsible. There are few authors' names announced and those that are, are in most cases *noms de plume*.

John Edmund Fordwych was not the real name of the man who wrote, in the early years of this century, a series of great human dramas such as *Daddy* and who, as an editor, later became the greatest purveyor of juvenile literature in the world. The pseudonym, Edwin Forrester, author of *Tom-All-Alone*, hid the identity of a Civil Servant, who, for all the years it ran, wrote *The Red Rovers*. This was his first commission; a football story 'just to run through the winter programme,' said the editor. To young Edwin Forrester this commission meant a great deal for there was a baby on the way at home, but, even so, it meant far more than either he or the editor could possibly have foreseen. For that story 'just to run through the winter programme' proved so popular that it ran for over twenty years and with its 2,000,000 odd words was probably the world's longest serial story. Other authors wrote under their own names . . . S. Clarke Hook, author of 'Jack, Sam and Pete' stories, which in their day swept the country and will never be quite forgotten by those who read them, and Richard Starr whose detective stories, prominent among which was *Slade of the Yard*, were afterwards published in novel form and were popular with a wider public. There is one name that cannot be left out of such a chronicle as this: Charles Hamilton, creator of the immortal school stories which appeared in *The Gem* and *The Magnet*. And yet, in this case, it is by his pen names of Frank Richards, Owen Conquest, and Martin Clifford that his public knew him.

The paper shortage brought about by the war caused the cessation of publication of the stories of Greyfriars and St. Jims, but letters to the publishers are proof that Tom Merry and Co. and Harry Wharton and his chums are not forgotten. One character from among the many created still lives on, for the adventures of Billy Bunter, in picture story form, are now entertaining a new generation of readers.

Artists even more than authors have remained anonymous, but there is one who will always be remembered under his own name. Tom

Browne, R.B.A., R.I., was one of the leading caricaturists of his time, and made Weary Willie and Tired Tim of *Chips* so famous that they are household names. Only recently, and for by no means the first time, they were mentioned in Parliamentary debate. Tom Browne died in 1910 but Weary Willie and Tired Tim still go their merry way. Casey Court, that Cockney panorama of juvenile inventiveness and make-believe is also still with us.

If there is one pictorial character which stands out above all others in memories of young reading, it is Tiger Tim who with his companions, the Bruin Boys, first appeared in a juvenile periodical when Number One of *The Rainbow* was issued in 1914.

Tiger Tim . . . how was the character born? Who invented the name? In this case the character was born some time before it appeared regularly in *The Rainbow* and it was born by accident! That well-known illustrator, the Irishman, J. Louis Smythe, was called upon by an

IN THE VERNACULAR, THIS WAS 'A JAPE'; THE VICTIM, OF COURSE, THE SWELL OF ST. JIM'S.

editor to picture an incident from a story. The passage chosen was where the heroine stepped from her carriage and entered a house . . . 'followed by her tiger, Tim'. And Louis Smythe, unaware of the fact that in this instance a 'tiger' signified a page-boy or youthful attendant, drew instead a small, striped tiger promenading serenely upright upon its hind legs. The editor gasped, laughed, but mentally noted for future use a new and attractive character. How attractive that character was can be vouched for by the generations who since then have enjoyed his picture and story adventures.

Among the authors and artists and editorial staffs who combine in the presentation of these periodical and annual adventures there always have been men and women who are well known in the world of art and letters. And if there is one characteristic they all have in common, that is sincerity. Without sincerity they could not hold their public for one moment; without a genuine understanding and love of young people they would, sooner or later, offend the feelings of their readers.

In spite of the fact that so few people are named in the issues of the weekly and annual publications the post bag to editors and characters is very heavy. The requests for Tiger Tim and the Bruin Boys to attend Christmas and birthday parties come in all the year round. Every such one is unfailingly answered, explaining in the nicest way possible that for Tiger Tim to attend every function would mean that he could scarcely ever be at school or at home and that, as it would not be fair for him to attend some and not others, there is nothing for it but that he should attend none. At Christmas time especially the letters to the editors are numerous. So many young readers credit editors with powers equal to legendary Father Christmas or regard them as forwarding agents to that enchanting personality. One character, that of Sammy the Stork, is quite often asked to supply a little brother or sister. What heart-ache lay behind the letter to Sammy which said: ' I am very lonely so will you please send me soon a little brother named John to play with.'

All letters do not present such problems in the way of an answer as, for instance, the one from an Army officer, a member of a well-known military club. Following the removal of a character named Tom the Menagerie Man from the programme of a periodical, he wrote in, appealing most sincerely for Tom's reinstatement. This character had taken his fancy when young and, although come to man's estate, he

had continued to buy the paper regularly ever since, in order to enjoy Tom's picture adventures.

At one time it was the custom to present to old regular readers of some weekly journals a hand-coloured certificate recording their loyalty; it was announced that this would be accompanied by a five shilling honorarium. When making application for this much-prized certificate one reader stated that as he could play no musical instrument he would much prefer the five shillings to the honorarium! In this case the editor concerned was happy to grant his reader's request.

Sometimes the post bag will contain letters of criticism as when, during the recent war, a coloured G.I. wrote complaining about the publication of the adventures of a Nigger Boy. He was under the firm impression that this was a slight to all such as he and was published with the sole purpose of destroying Anglo-American friendship.

A study of these periodicals and annuals over the years discloses the fact that, apart from the editor, the most publicised personality is the office boy. An early example of management and staff co-operation!

Doyen of the office boys is Philpott Bottles who, in the space he reserves for himself each week, gives his views upon the most important topic of the week, as he sees it. His choice of subjects is as varied as his spelling, his findings often disconcertingly logical. In a recent article he put forward with some warmth his claim to public acknowledgement as the originator of the Nu Spelling now before the public in all the glory of official recognition. For, as he says, has he not been spelling that way for years?

If you, my reader, have a mind for a little mental exercise of an unusual type, I would suggest you select a character from among your memories and work out for him or her an idea that author or artist could turn into the finished article. What will you need? Good-natured fun, a touch of drama and excitement, a modicum of mystery, unexpected twists of plot or character to raise a laugh or gain a thrill, an appeal to the heart and all surrounded with atmosphere to suit. Blend together with simplicity and sincerity, have right triumphant over wrong and bring to a happy ending.

A happy ending! Happy ever afterwards! Maybe that is the great secret . . . maybe not. But there is no denying that for generations of children and for those of us who retain the freshness of childhood in our hearts there is endless happiness in Christmas Numbers.

The Christmas Dinner

BY WASHINGTON IRVING

Twenty years before Dickens began to lay the foundations of the modern Christmas tradition in England, Washington Irving was doing so in America. Dickens actually admitted 'I don't go upstairs two nights out of seven without taking Washington Irving under my arm.' All of Irving's Christmas sketches were, however, written in England, though first published in New York. The Christmas Dinner, presented here slightly abridged, was 'pronounced by some as out of date' as a true picture of old-fashioned Christmas even in 1819, the year of its publication. But a hundred and thirty years later, that is neither here nor there.

HE DINNER was served up in the great hall, where the squire always held his Christmas banquet. A blazing, crackling fire of logs had been heaped on to warm the spacious apartment, and the flame went sparkling and wreathing up the wide-mouthed chimney. The great picture of the crusader and his white horse had been profusely decorated with greens for the occasion; and holly and ivy had likewise been wreathed round the helmet and weapons on the opposite wall, which I understand were the arms of the same warrior. A sideboard was set out just under this chivalric trophy, on which was a display of plate that might have vied (at least in variety) with Belshazzar's parade of the vessels of the temple: 'flagons, cans, cups, beakers, goblets, basins, and ewers'; the gorgeous utensils of good companionship that had gradually accumulated through many generations of jovial house-keepers. Before these stood the two Yule candles, beaming like two stars of the first magnitude; other lights were distributed in branches, and the whole array glittered like a firmament of silver.

The parson said grace, which was not a short familiar one, such as is commonly addressed to the Deity in these unceremonious days; but a long courtly, well-worded one of the ancient school. There was now a pause, as if something was expected; when suddenly the butler entered the hall with some degree of bustle: he was attended by a servant on each side with a large wax-light and bore a silver dish, on which was an enormous pig's head, decorated with rosemary, with a lemon in its mouth, which was placed with great formality at the head of the table. The moment this pageant made its appearance, the harper struck up a flourish; at the conclusion of which a young Oxonian, on receiving a hint from the squire, gave, with an air of the most comic gravity, an old carol, the first verse of which was as follows:

> *Caput apri defero,*
> *Reddens laudes Domino.*
> *The boar's head in hand bring I,*
> *With garlands gay and rosemary.*
> *I pray you all synge merily*
> *Qui estis in convivio.*

Though prepared to witness many of these little eccentricities, from being apprized of the peculiar hobby of mine host; yet, I confess, the parade with which so odd a dish was introduced somewhat perplexed me, until I gathered from the conversation of the squire and the parson, that it was meant to represent the bringing in of the boar's head; a dish formerly served up with much ceremony and the sound of minstrelsy and song, at great tables, on Christmas day. ' I like the old custom,' said the squire, ' not merely because it is stately and pleasing in itself, but because it was observed at the college at Oxford at which I was educated. When I hear the old song chanted, it brings back to mind the time when I was young and gamesome—and the noble old college hall—and my fellow-students loitering about in their black gowns; many of whom, poor lads, are now in their graves! '

The table was literally loaded with good cheer, and presented an epitome of country abundance, in this season of overflowing larders. A distinguished post was allotted to ' ancient sirloin ', as mine host termed it; being, as he added, ' the standard of old English hospitality, and a joint of goodly presence, and full of expectation '. There were several dishes quaintly decorated, and which had evidently something traditional in their embellishments; but about which, as I did not like to appear over-curious, I asked no questions.

I could not, however, but notice a pie, magnificently decorated with peacocks' feathers, in the imitation of the tail of that bird, which overshadowed a considerable tract of the table. This, the squire confessed, with some little hesitation, was a pheasant pie, though a peacock pie was certainly the most authentical; but there had been such a mortality among the peacocks this season, that he could not prevail upon himself to have one killed.

When the cloth was removed, the butler brought in a huge silver vessel of rare and curious workmanship, which he placed before the squire. Its appearance was hailed with acclamation; being the Wassail Bowl, so renowned in Christmas festivity. The contents had been prepared by the squire himself; for it was a beverage in the skilful mixture of which he particularly prided himself; alleging that it was too abstruse and complex for the comprehension of an ordinary servant. It was a potation, indeed, that might well make the heart of a toper leap within him; being composed of the richest and raciest wines, highly spiced and sweetened, with roasted apples bobbing about the surface.

The old gentleman's whole countenance beamed with a serene look of indwelling light, as he stirred this mighty bowl. Having raised it to his lips, with a hearty wish of a merry Christmas to all present, he sent it brimming round the board, for everyone to follow his example, according to the primitive style; pronouncing it ' the ancient fountain of good-feeling, where all hearts met together '.

There was much laughing and rallying as the honest emblem of Christmas joviality circulated, and was kissed rather coyly by the ladies. When it reached Master Simon, he raised it in both hands, and with the air of a boon companion struck up an old Wassail chanson.

When the ladies had retired, the conversation, as usual, became still more animated; many good things were broached which had been thought of during dinner, but which would not exactly do for a lady's ear; and though I cannot positively affirm that there was much wit uttered, yet I have certainly heard many contests of rare wit produce much less laughter. Wit, after all, is a mighty, tart, pungent, ingredient, and much too acid for some stomachs; but honest good humour is the oil and wine of a merry meeting, and there is no jovial companionship equal to that where jokes are rather small, and laughter abundant.

The squire told several long stories of early college pranks and adventures, in some of which the parson had been a sharer; though in looking at the latter, it required some effort of imagination to figure such a little dark anatomy of a man into the perpetrator of a madcap gambol.

I found the tide of wine and wassail fast gaining on the dry land of sober judgement. The company grew merrier and louder as their jokes grew duller. Master Simon was in as chirping a humour as a grasshopper filled with dew; his old songs grew of a warmer complexion, and he began to talk maudlin. He even gave a long song about the wooing of a widow.

This song inspired a fat-headed old gentleman, who made several attempts to tell rather a broad story out of Joe Miller, that was pat to the purpose; but he always stuck in the middle, everybody recollecting the latter part excepting himself. The parson, too, began to show the effects of good cheer, having gradually settled down into a doze, and his wig sitting most suspiciously on one side. Just at this juncture we were summoned to the drawing-room, and I suspect, at the private instigation of mine host, whose joviality seemed always tempered with a proper love of decorum.

After the dinner table was removed, the hall was given up to the youngest members of the family, who, prompted to all kinds of noisy mirth by the Oxonian and Master Simon, made its old walls ring with their merriment, as they played at romping games. I delight in the witnessing the gambols of children, and particularly at this happy holiday season, and could not help stealing out of the drawing-room on hearing one of their peals of laughter. I found them at the game of blind-man's-buff.

Master Simon, who was the leader of their revels, and seemed on all occasions to fulfil the office of that ancient potentate, the Lord of Misrule, was blinded in the midst of the hall. The little beings were as busy about him as the mock fairies about Falstaff; pinching him, plucking at the skirts of his coat, and tickling him with straws. One fine blue-eyed girl of about thirteen, with her flaxen hair all in beautiful confusion, her frolic face in a glow, her frock half torn off her shoulders, a complete picture of a romp, was the chief tormentor; and, from the slyness with which Master Simon avoided the smaller game, and hemmed this wild little nymph in corners, and obliged her to jump shrieking over chairs, I suspected the rogue of being not a whit more blinded than was convenient.

When I returned to the drawing-room, I found the company seated round the fire listening to the parson, who gave several anecdotes of the fancies of the neighbouring peasantry, concerning the effigy of the crusader, which lay on the tomb by the church altar. As it was the only monument of the kind in that part of the country, it had always been regarded with feelings of superstition by the good wives of the village. It was said to get up from the tomb and walk the rounds of the church-yard on stormy nights, particularly when it thundered; and one old woman whose cottage bordered on the churchyard, had seen it through the windows of the church, when the moon shone, slowly pacing up and down the aisles. It was the belief that some wrong had been left unredressed by the deceased, or some treasure hidden, which kept the spirit in a state of trouble and restlessness. Some talked of gold and jewels buried in the tomb, over which the spectre kept watch; and there was a story current of a sexton in old times who endeavoured to break his way to the coffin at night, but, just as he reached it, received a violent blow from the marble hand of the effigy, which stretched him senseless on the pavement. These tales were often laughed at by some of the sturdier among the rustics, yet when night came on, there were some of the stoutest unbelievers that were shy of venturing alone in the footpath that led across the churchyard.

Whilst we were all attention to the parson's stories, our ears were suddenly assailed by a burst of heterogeneous sounds from the hall. The door suddenly flew open, and a train came trooping into the room, that might have been mistaken for the breaking-up of the court of Fairy. That indefatigable spirit, Master Simon, in the faithful discharge of his duties as Lord of Misrule, had conceived the idea of a Christmas mummery or masking; and having called in to his assistance the Oxonian and a young officer, who were equally ripe for anything that should occasion romping and merriment, they had carried it into instant effect. The old housekeeper had been consulted; the antique clothes-presses and wardrobes rummaged, and made to yield up the relics of finery that had not seen the light for several generations; the younger part of the company had been privately convened from the parlour and hall, and the whole had been bedizened out into a burlesque imitation of an antique mask.

Master Simon led the van, as 'Ancient Christmas', quaintly apparelled in a ruff, a short cloak, which had very much the aspect of one of the old housekeeper's petticoats, and a hat that might have served for a village steeple, and must indubitably have figured in the days of the Covenanters. From under this his nose curved boldly forth flushed with a frost-bitten bloom, that seemed the very trophy of a December blast. He was accompanied by the blue-eyed romp, dished up as 'Dame Mince Pie', in the venerable magnificence of a faded brocade, long stomacher, peaked hat, and high heeled shoes. The rest of the train had been metamorphosed in various ways and the irruption of this motley crew, with beat of drum, according to ancient custom, was the consummation of uproar and merriment. Master Simon covered himself with glory by the stateliness with which, as Ancient Christmas, he walked a minuet with the peerless, though giggling, Dame Mince Pie. It was followed by a dance of all the characters, which, from its medley of costumes, seemed as though the old family portraits had skipped down from their frames to join in the sport.

The worthy squire contemplated these fantastic sports, and this resurrection of his wardrobe, with the simple relish of childish delight. He stood chuckling and rubbing his hands, and scarcely hearing a word the parson said, notwithstanding that the latter was discoursing most authentically on the ancient and stately dance of the Paon, or peacock, from which he conceived the minuet to be derived. For my part I was in a continual excitement, from the varied scenes of whim and innocent gaiety passing before me. It was inspiring to me to see wild-eyed frolic and warm-hearted hospitality breaking out from among the chills and glooms of the winter, and old age throwing off his apathy, and catching once more the freshness of youthful enjoyment.

I felt also an interest in the scene, from the consideration that these fleeting customs were posting fast into oblivion, and that this was, perhaps, the only family in England in which the whole of them were still punctiliously observed. There was a quaintness, too, mingled with all this revelry, that gave it a peculiar zest: it was suited to the time and place; and as the old manor-house almost reeled with mirth and wassail, it seemed echoing back the joviality of long-departed years.

REGENCY
Christmas

BY ABOUT 1845 the stage was set for the
sentimental Christmas familiar to us but
almost unknown to the Georgians. These
prints of the years preceding Victoria
show the Regency wags poking fun at
Christmas with all their usual brutality.

A MERRY CHRISTMAS

A MERRY CHRISTMAS AND A HAPPY NEW YEAR

THE SAME TO YOU SIR, AND MANY OF 'EM

CHRISTMAS CAROLS

CHRISTMAS CAROLS

'Well, Mr. Crow, I hope we have not kept your Master waiting dinner.'
'Oh, no—Massa gone out o' town, but him leave word he wish you ALL a
Merry Christmas.'

FLOWERS OF LOVELINESS: SNOWDROP

SNOWBALLS — OR THE OLD BUCK IN DISTRESS

By way of a postscript, it is interesting to compare the outlook of the early nineteenth century humorists with those of today, for it is curiously like and both are totally dissimilar from the Victorian and Edwardian cartoonists who rarely mocked at Christmas. In *Christmas with the Cartoonists* on another page of THE CHRISTMAS BOOK, the drawings by Osbert Lancaster (1946) and Giles (1945) are direct descendants of 'Christmas Carols.' (1835). Basically, they are the same joke, the social significance gone, the savagery replaced by a charming and gentle malice.

New-Fashioned Christmas

BY ALDOUS HUXLEY

HE NAME is still the same; but the thing is almost unrecognisably different from what Charles Dickens meant by 'Christmas'. For example, there was no tree at Dingley Dell, and, except for five shillings to Sam Weller, not a single present was given. Christmas, for Mr. Pickwick and his friends, was an affair of copious eating and still more copious drinking, interrupted by bouts of home-made fun and purely domestic horseplay.

For us, three generations later, the word connotes the Prince Consort's imported Teutonic evergreen; connotes all those endless presents, which it is such a burden to buy and such an embarrassment to receive; connotes restaurants, dance halls, theatres, cabarets—all the highly organised professional entertainments provided by the austere business-men who run the amusement industry. Only the name connects the new-fashioned Christmas with the Pickwickian festival.

The tree, of course, was a mere accident. If Queen Victoria had married a Frenchman we should probably be giving one another *étrennes* and ushering in the year with a series of calls on the most remote and most personally antipathetic of our innumerable relations. (Relations, in France, *are* innumerable.) As it was, she took to herself a prince from the land of tannenbaums. It is therefore to a tannenbaum's green branches, and upon Christmas Day, that we attach our gifts.

The tree, I repeat, was an accident, a thing outside the realm of determinism, a product of personal idiosyncrasy. But all the other changes in our Christmas habits, which have taken place since Dickens wrote of Dingley Dell, are the results of great impersonal processes. During Dickens's life-time, and still more rapidly after his death, industrial production enormously and continuously increased. But production cannot increase unless there is a corresponding increase in consumption. It became necessary to stimulate consumption, to provide the home public with reasons, or, better still, with compelling unreasons, for consuming. Hence the rise of advertisement, and hence the gradual and, as time went on, the more and more deliberate canalisation into industrially profitable channels of all such common human impulses and emotions as lent themselves to the process.

The producer who succeeds in thus canalising some universal human urge opens up for himself and his successors an inexhaustible gold mine. Thus, art and industry have flourished from time immemorial in the rich soil of bereavement and the fear of death. Weddings have been almost as profitable to commerce as funerals, and within the last few years an American man of genius has discovered how even filial affection may be made a justification for increased consumption; the florists and candy manufacturers of the United States have reason to bless the inventor of Mother's Day.

The love of excitement is as deeply planted in human nature as the love of a mother; the desire for change, for novelty, for a relief from the monotony of every day, as strong as sexual desire or the terror of death. Men have instituted festivals and holidays to satisfy these cravings. Mr. Pickwick's Christmas was a typical feast day of the old style—a time of jollification and excitement, a gaudily glittering ' captain jewel in the carcanet' of grey, uneventful days. Psychologically, it performed its function. Not economically, however—that is, so far as *we* are concerned. The Pickwickian Christmas did very little to stimulate consumption; it was mainly a gratuitous festivity. A few vintners and distillers and poulterers were the only people whom it greatly profited financially. This was a state of things which an ever-increasingly efficient industrialism could not possible afford to tolerate. Christmas, accordingly, was canalised. The deep festal impulse of man was harnessed and made to turn a very respectable little wheel in the mills of industry. Today Christmas is an important economic event. The distributors of goods spend large sums in advertising potential gifts, and (since the man who pays the piper calls the tune) the newspapers reinforce their advertisement by fostering a notion that the mutual goodwill of modern Christians can be expressed only by the exchange of manufactured articles.

The last thirty years have witnessed the promotion of innkeeping and showmanship to the rank of major commercial enterprises. Major commercial enterprises spend money on advertising. Therefore, newspapers are always suggesting that a good time can be enjoyed only by those who take what is offered them by entertainment manufacturers. The Dickensian Christmas-at-Home receives only perfunctory lip-service from a Press which draws a steady income from the catering and amusement trades. Home-made fun is gratuitous, and gratuitousness is something which an industrialised world cannot afford to tolerate.

Christmas
in Charlotte Street

BY KATIE GANDY

IT WAS drawing near Christmas when I first met Mickey Jackson. I
was walking with a bag of buns down Charlotte Street, and there he
was: both feet planted firmly on the pavement, turning his large
brown face sideways to peer imploringly at each passer-by. Quite a
little crowd of sympathisers stood near—two small boys, a lady with
a scarlet umbrella, and an old man with a young fir-tree which Mickey
was vainly trying to nibble. All looked quite distraught with anxiety,
and all except Mickey, who was too busy munching, drew sighs of
sentimental relief when I had made the expected sacrifice. (One bun,
a quarter of a bread unit . . . it was really asking rather much.)

' I'm *so* glad you came!' confided the lady. ' I didn't know what we were going to do!'

The little boys beamed with satisfaction. They stood on tiptoe to pat Mickey's brown nose.

' 'E didn't ought to be up on the footpath, did he?' they commented, full of admiration. ' Giddown there, old fellow!'

Mickey paid not the smallest attention. He took a further pace forward, bringing with him the creaking van of W. Jackson, Carter, and fastened his brown eyes yearningly upon the paper bag. I decided it was time to go, and moved on just as Mr. Jackson emerged from the taproom of The Goat and Compasses, where he had been having a quick one. There were loud cries, snorts and shuffles, and a moment later the clatter of wheels over cobblestones as the Jackson equipage moved by at a spanking pace. Mr. Jackson wore a sort of leather pod over his head and was brandishing a whip kept quite obviously for display purposes only. Mickey himself was galloping up Charlotte Street at a pace that would have qualified him for the National. Showing off, on a pint of beer and a bun between them . . . but then, they were like that.

Mickey is not the only drayhorse I know; I am on nodding terms with several. This part of the city, lying next to the Docks and the river, is given over to warehouses, and outside the warehouses, all the way along the narrow streets, stand the horses; one behind another, waiting all day between the shafts of their tarpaulin-covered wagons with nothing to do except gaze dreamily into the tarpaulin-shrouded depths of the wagon in front. Charlotte Street is a recognised waiting-place for them; every day I pass the same horses in familiar attitudes of impatience or resignation. I should like to think of them as friends, but I am afraid that the friendship is one-sided, for they are remote, reserved creatures, and rarely turn to glance at a passer-by. In their great, lustrous eyes is an abstraction not to be charmed away by the gift of a nervously-offered carrot.

But as I say, Mickey is different. There is an eager friendliness about him that makes one wonder whether he realises that he is a horse at all. And although he is quite the shabbiest horse in the line, he is always absurdly jaunty. I don't know much about the toilette of a drayhorse, but comparing him with his colleagues, I cannot feel that Mr. Jackson really does him justice. More often than not he looks distinctly seedy; his brown mane is hopelessly tangled, a wispy beard dangles from his chin and his forelock is tied up with a piece of old string. It does seem a shame when all the others are so smart, but perhaps Mr. Jackson is too busy.

Mickey, of course, never complains; he is the last horse in the world to fall victim to an attack of self-pity. He looks at me over his nosebag, when I pass him at lunchtime, with an air that says, 'Behold me! Here I stand in this delightful street, on this delightful day, eating this very choice meal with all the relish it deserves! Observe the natty piece of sacking that is spread over my back and the ribbon that lends distinction to my tail! Pity me if you dare!'

The street is sunless and depressing, the sacking is threadbare and the ribbon (its presence is an astonishing accident) is faded to no colour at all, so that one suspects that it must be a relic of the Coronation. None of these things affects Mickey's dauntless optimism. It must be his sunny disposition that wins him so many friends; he is always receiving salutations from the lorry-drivers and warehousemen of the district. 'Well,' they say heartily, emerging from the coffee-house close by (and sometimes a piece of sugar changes hands), ''Ow are we today, old cock?'

And Mickey tosses his wisp of beard and pricks his ears in an expressive manner quite peculiar to himself, so that the acquaintance passes on more captivated than ever. He is the most popular horse in the neighbourhood.

There are other well-known characters in Charlotte Street. There is the tall piebald horse whose pitch is a few yards farther up and who wears a very becoming sort of metal tiara bearing the mystic letters L.M.S. A well-kept, somewhat military-looking character, this. He carries his polished brass headpiece proudly as if it were some sort of military decoration; he has a habit of tossing his head and snorting to himself, and he is subject to regrettable fits of contrariness. The other day I overheard a furious altercation between himself and his driver, a kindly, red-faced man absolutely devoted to his welfare. (I have seen him, in snowy weather, crawling round on all fours in order to equip his charge with sackcloth bootees.) But for once the driver's patience seemed to be exhausted. He was scarlet in the face and furious. 'I'll *slosh* you!' he cried, wrestling with a piece of harness.

I left them still wrangling, the horse pulling one way in a fit of senseless obstinacy, his driver—to the accompaniment of a perfect storm of angry language—tugging in the other direction. It was like a lovers' quarrel. But they must have made it up quickly, for when I passed them next morning they were on terms of the greatest amiability, the driver leaning with a friendly arm around his charge's neck, and the charge himself standing in a characteristic attitude, one foreleg stiffly extended. It is his favourite pose, and makes him look like a ballet-dancer.

Then there is Jacko, the great black-velvety creature attached to the van of W. Jenks, Carter. Jacko Jenks has the most appealing soft dark eyes of any horse on the road. His favourite hobby is thinking, and he spends much time gazing abstractedly into the interior of the van in front of him, where there is usually nothing to be seen but a quantity of straw or a pile of packing cases; but he will occasionally come down to earth and condescend to take a piece of sugar from one of his many admirers. I have seen him receive at least three in quick succession, and I have also seen him devour a luscious brown orchid pinned to the collar of a rich acquaintance, since when my faith in him has been a little shaken. Jacko is the acknowledged social leader of the neighbourhood and has only two rivals, a pair of powerful whites who pull a coal-cart and remain spotless in spite of this handicap. Between these three horses, where appearance is concerned, there is little to choose; all three wear glittering brass ornaments, all have coats of silken perfection, all possess wonderful manes and tails that are interwoven daily with fresh straw and twined with many coloured ribbons. Beside them, poor old Mickey Jackson has the humble air of having fallen on evil times.

It was Christmas Eve when I last went down Charlotte Street. There had been a fine sunset, and a peachy dusk was lingering over the warehouses. The street was thronged with people hurrying in the direction of the railway station, and even amongst the horses the spirit of Christmas was apparent.

I met all my old friends. The two white coal-horses pranced gaily down the street in front of their empty wagon. They wore wreaths of laurel on their proud heads in addition to the usual bells and ribbons; their driver, swaying on his lofty perch, might have been a Roman general returning from a victorious campaign. They passed with a jingling of bells and a clatter of hoofs on the cobblestones, and mine was not the only head to turn after them.

The next horse I encountered was Jacko Jenks, a perfect Christmas tree. Two pink chrysanthemums were entwined in his silky forelock and tied in place with a piece of pink ribbon. His mane was festooned with evergreen and powdered with pellets of cotton-wool, and red and green ribbons decorated his handsome tail. I wished him a happy Christmas and went on, past the long file of waiting horses, all paying their tribute to the season in the form of sprigs of holly or paper streamers. I looked for my special favourite, for whom I had a small Christmas present wrapped in a piece of paper, but he was nowhere to be seen. I concluded that he must have been sent on some special mission and would not be back until late, but as I was turning out of Charlotte Street a cart came rattling along and drew up sharply at the traffic-lights.

There was no mistaking that ridiculous tuft of beard. I presented my gift, a juicy carrot, which he accepted with alacrity; and as he was munching it I caught the expression in his eyes. For the first time since I had known him, there was a hint of superiority in his bearing.

' Seen my decorations? ' he said.

Then the traffic signals turned from red to green and in less than a second he was off again; but not before I had had time to realise what he meant. Perched on the top of his unkempt head and quite obviously retrieved from the pavement was a small, crushed, yellowish sprig of mistletoe. In its centre was one perfect berry.

' Happy Christmas! ' I called after the departing vehicle. Mr. Jackson returned by wishing me, very cordially, the compliments of the season. My friend bent his attention on the road in front; but there was a world of meaning in the way he twitched his left ear.

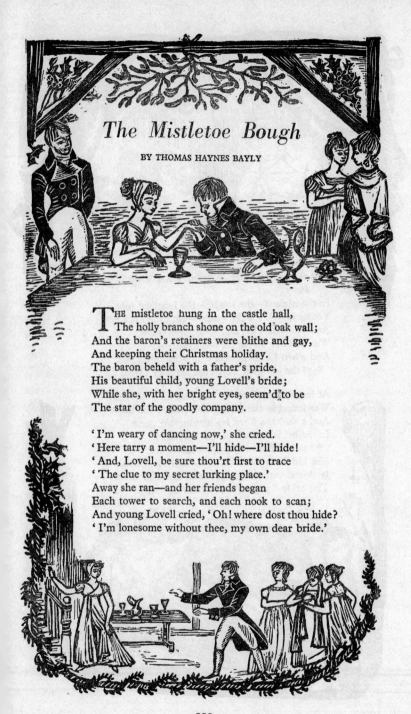

The Mistletoe Bough

BY THOMAS HAYNES BAYLY

THE mistletoe hung in the castle hall,
The holly branch shone on the old oak wall;
And the baron's retainers were blithe and gay,
And keeping their Christmas holiday.
The baron beheld with a father's pride,
His beautiful child, young Lovell's bride;
While she, with her bright eyes, seem'd to be
The star of the goodly company.

' I'm weary of dancing now,' she cried.
' Here tarry a moment—I'll hide—I'll hide!
' And, Lovell, be sure thou'rt first to trace
' The clue to my secret lurking place.'
Away she ran—and her friends began
Each tower to search, and each nook to scan;
And young Lovell cried, ' Oh! where dost thou hide?
' I'm lonesome without thee, my own dear bride.'

They sought her that night! and they sought her
    next day!
And they sought her in vain, when a week pass'd
    away!
In the highest—the lowest—the loneliest spot,
Young Lovell sought wildly—but found her not.
And years flew by, and their grief at last
Was told as a sorrowful tale long past;
And when Lovell appear'd the children cried,
' See! the old man weeps for his fairy bride.'

At length an oak chest, that had long lain hid
Was found in the castle—they raised the lid—
And a skeleton form lay mouldering there,
In the bridal wreath of that lady fair!
Oh! sad was her fate!—in sportive jest
She hid from her lord in the old oak chest,
It closed with a spring!—and, dreadful doom,
The bride lay clasp'd in her living tomb!

Stranger in the Snow

BY KAY BOYLE

REMEMBER the tree that we trimmed in the forest in France on Christmas morning. It was a tree for the wild birds to come to, and we hung it with suet and corn and currant cake, for France was still a rich country then, and you could buy these things at will. That was a cold year; it was one of the bitterest years in France's history, and the children kept watch over the tree, two by two, and drove the ravens away. There were a great many different kinds of birds that came to eat there—mountain finches with yellow or rust-coloured breasts, and wild pigeons. But it could never be explained how the heron came there; he drifted down through the needle trees as silently as a leaf might have fallen at another altitude, and there he stood, bleak and motionless, in the snow. He was a blue heron child, perhaps dropped out of the ruthless passage of migration, held upright on one leg, with his mouth tight-lipped, sardonic, in his evil face.

'Merry Christmas,' the children said to him, but he would have none of it. He was thinking of Mediterranean waters and the sleek bodies of southern fish, and his heart was breaking in him. The aigrettes that he wore hung sideways from his topknot, and he peered from under them with an eye as vicious as a snake's. The claws of his lifted, naked foot were drawn up beneath his breast in an icy, mailed fist, and if he had come to the Christmas tree for food, he did not turn his head towards the sight of France's bounty hanging on the branches.

'He can live all winter in the kitchen,' the children said, and they picked him up. There were three boys, Roger and Raymond and Maurice, sons of the peasant mountaineers, and the little girl watched everything they did.

III

' I have some postcards of Casablanca," Raymond said. ' I can put them up for him on the wall.'

' Except they only show the main street with a tramway on it, and a view of the harbour. He'd like a view of the desert,' said Maurice, and as they started off towards home, he took the little girl's hand.

' And in the spring,' Roger went on with it, ' we can take a voyage to a warmer place. We can go to the jungle and let him go free when we get there. He's the best Christmas present we've ever had because we didn't expect him,' he said, and the heron looked out at them, from the cloak they had wrapped him in, with hooded, venomous eyes.

On the way back to the village in the snow, the little girl sang a song to him. She did not speak any language very well yet, but she knew the tune, and she sang the song over and over, each time a little louder, as if each breath of it would blow strength into the fire that would serve to warm him.

> ' *Jingus bell, jingus bell,*' she sang,
> ' *Jingus all wid hay.*
> *Oze wad funny funny tied*
> *Ten hose open legs.*'

That was eight years ago, and there have been Christmasses in France since then, but they have not been the same kind of Christmasses. That Christmas the children made a bed for the heron by the stove, but he never relented. He would take the glutinous food of rice water or barley water and milk from the medicine dropper, and a pearl of the priceless stuff would hang upon his beak. The length of his throat would swallow it down, but the taste of it was nothing to him. It slid like quick-silver through his body, while his tongue moved, sharp as a fingernail and black with venom. The afternoon he died, Maurice's mother came into the kitchen.

' When birds are about to go, they all do it the same: they stretch their wings out and they flap them terribly,' she said, and that is what the heron did. From the sound of his wings, it might have been that he had risen from his bed in a wonderful pure arc of flight, and yet he had not risen. He lay forward upon the sharp point of his breast, his long neck stretched, his beak upon the floor, and his eyes were closed upon the panorama of palm and cactus flower and fluted sand, and his wings beat powerfully in the unsullied vision of ascent. It was

early in January that Roger and Raymond and Maurice buried him—
not in the ground, for it was too well hidden to reach with any imple-
ment, but in the depths of mountain snow.

The heron was not advised by any higher court that he was about
to die. Therefore he did not have the opportunity to write a farewell
letter to anybody at all. On the morning of the day he was to thresh
his wings in simulated flight, he did not set down the following words:

' My dearest parents: For me everything is over. I appeared
before the German military court an hour ago and was condemned
to death with two of my comrades. Mama, Papa, I ask your pardon
for all the trouble and distress that I have caused you. Please stay
happy and gay so that you may live a long time. It is so foolish to die,
like me, at eighteen. Please have my photograph enlarged and put it
up beside the radio. I shall always be your little boy who caused
you so much pain.'

The signature was Roger's, and the date was Christmas, 1943, and
he had added a postscript to the letter, saying:

' Please write to the German military court for my body and take
me home.'

Roger, like Raymond and Maurice, was permitted the final cigarette,
the half-hour with the priest, the scrap of paper on which to write, the
time to prepare for an occasion in which he had not planned to partici-
pate.

' I do not know how I dare write you that I am to be executed,'
Raymond wrote. ' Please do not put up a monument for me—just
a small tombstone, like a soldier's.'

And he ended this letter to his father:

' I wish you a happy and prosperous New Year.'

Maurice was the youngest of them, and he wrote:

' I cannot think of anything to say.'

For in the spring of 1940, two things happened which none of us had
expected. France was invaded, and by May it was clear that France
was defeated; and almost at once the ferocious hunger of the body

and the ferocious hunger of the spirit began to take the children away. The second thing that happened was a small thing in comparison to this—it was like a single word spoken in a foreign tongue, and the meaning of it has never been made quite clear. The heron had been buried deep under the snow in the early days of January, and no one gave him a thought now. And then one day in the spring, as we climbed the mountain to the cattle refuge, there he lay on the bright new grass which the snow had left behind. He had not faded through the winter; his feathers were as blue as they had been the afternoon the children dug the grave for him; he had been enamelled and embalmed in brilliance by the depths of cold. He had not altered, except now his eyes were open. He had drawn the delicate little curtains of silk down in order to see in his solitude the things that he had perished for—the vegetation that did not flourish in this part of the world, the sweet, rotting fruit, the reeds that grew tall and thick in the tropical waters.

Raymond and Roger and Maurice were alive that spring, and they made him a raft of pine bark, and they spread crocuses on the raft, nearly colourless ones, with roots still icy from the winter, and they laid the heron on the crocus heads. The little girl stood holding Maurice's hand while the raft with the bird on it set out on the current of the mountain stream.

' He's the only Christmas present that didn't get broken,' she said, and we watched the water bear him quickly away.

CHRISTMAS

trimmings

BY CONSTANCE SPRY

Bare walls make giddy housewives

He doeth much that doeth a thing well

All is gay that is green

1

The Kissing Bunch and other Fancies

O YOU REMEMBER what, in childhood's Christmas days, drew from you that ultimate small sigh of pleasure: that surprised, unconscious sound which from a sensitive child denotes aesthetic satisfaction?

If you can summon that memory, enhanced now by time, and build around it in planning your Christmas decorations you will almost certainly achieve success. Nor need you differentiate very much between what you shall have for the children and what for the grown-ups; sophistication and childishness have a meeting ground in Christmas ' nonsense'.

It was the miracle of the frost that held me spellbound, rime-edged leaf and branch, and jewellery of glittered seedhead; crystal patterns on the window-pane and icicles. So now my first choice is for something frosted, glistening and fairy-like, either for the tree, for the table or for general decoration. The basic material may be of the simplest: shapely bare twigs and seedheads, just touched with white paint and then heavily frosted will by themselves make Christmas groups, and for a table centre you may choose to add a few white flowers among these. Most lovely to my mind for the table is an arrangement of Christmas roses and ivy, the leaves and trails not covered, but heavily outlined and veined with frost and the whole glimmering in candlelight. To extend the decoration, trails of the glittered ivy may be wound around base and stem of the candelabra or form a wreath round the base of a single candle.

Another effective centrepiece is made with glittering leaves, cones, gourds, acorns and horse chestnuts, the two last wired together in bunches and all arranged like a Flemish still life of fruit. They may be piled up on a shallow tray in which you have tied wire netting or you may like to use a basket thickly bound with twisted cellophane. This makes a particularly suitable container for white and silver decorations and you may add little baskets of the same material to hold sweetmeats or Christmas posies for each guest.[1]

When it was possible to buy inexpensive bright fabrics for the Christmas table-cloth, much of the decorative effect was already gained. Silver gauze, scarlet lace, bright gauzy ribbons joined together like a rainbow, tarlatan in every colour, all came in for covering the table. Even on the most formal of polished tables, silver ribbon could well be used in association with white flowers. But now, what have we? Rags and tatters, years old, and nothing to buy. So again we must contrive. An old damask cloth dyed bright red, a length of hessian dyed to a darker shade are not too bad as a basis. Dancing figures, cut out of coloured paper can be laid on the cloth in patterns. Silver or gold paper of a satisfactory substantial quality is on the market again and big table mats cut out of this are effective; so is a length cut out in a lacy pattern running down the extent of the table. What would be condemned as tawdry at any other season may be considered gay at Christmas time.

Decorated candelabra or candlesticks are always effective. I found it worth while to have a pair of three-branch candelabra made in thick wire and these give scope for a variety of adornment. Failing this you may use your silver ones but will be well advised to twist some cotton wool thinly around them where the fastenings may scratch the silver.

For a frosted and glittered decoration I bind my wire candelabra with cellophane and then treat them in a variety of ways, the simplest being to fasten on to the main stem a spray of glittered evergreen. This may be supplemented by thin plaits of cellophane taken from arm to arm as though they were chains of glass.

For children you may like to make cellophane dolls holding posies of holly or mistletoe and fasten these to the base of each candlestick.

---

[1] On pages 124 to 128 Mrs. Spry describes in detail how this, and the other types of Christmas decorations she mentions may be made.

These are not difficult to contrive, as will be seen later, and are most effective.

For a holly table the candelabra are particularly good. Sprays of holly, green and variegated, well glittered, are fastened to the stem of each candelabrum and little wreaths of leaves arranged round the base of the candles. One needs plenty of berries in proportion to foliage so it is as well to strip the leaves of a few well berried stems and to mix these among the others.

If there are high candelabra a low centrepiece may be called for: two round Victorian posies of holly with paper frills lying back to back on a mirror look well and the ribbons which tie them may be allowed to lie down the length of the table. If there is not a suitable mirror available, a piece of glass over a sheet of silver paper will serve.

Children all seem to love a snow scene arranged on a mirror as a centrepiece with cotton wool hills and snowmen and looking-glass lakes and skating figures. I once made a ring of cellophane ballerinas round the mirror lake. They had little glittered head-dresses and appeared to dance over the snow. It is possible to use the same idea enlarged and translated in many ways.

It is a good plan to concentrate one's decorative efforts rather than to eke them out over a whole room. One good vase of flowers well planned is generally more effective than a number of small ones or one picture than twenty picture postcards. So, choosing the fireplace as the focal point, the snow scene is adopted as the main theme of decoration. The one I am about to describe stood over a cotton-wool-glittered snow chimney-piece and was flanked by two Staffordshire Red Riding Hood vases holding holly with lots of berries. It was made on a sheet of glass twenty-four inches long by twenty inches high, framed in silver paper, or rather in gummed paper silvered, the corners trimmed with sprays of holly. Ribbons hanging from a nail gave the illusion that the picture hung but it really stood on the mantel.

The scene was of snowy mountains, cellophane cascades and streams, glittering fir trees, stars and moon and a high castle on top of a mountain. In the foreground was a royal sleigh cut out of coloured paper drawn by a cut-out horse (so grandly draped that weakness in equestrian draughtmanship was fortunately disguised). The ermine cloaked and bonneted lady sat in her sleigh carrying holly, and behind her a negro postillion in brilliant colours carried her Christmas parcels. It was all made of cut-outs, cotton wool, silver and gold paper, tinsel and sequins. Any intelligent child can make something on these lines, varying the theme with Red Riding Hood, Cinderella or what you will. I may say that this particular piece of nonsense has, in common with the small boy's toy train, an advantage for grown-ups: they get a lot of fun out of playing with it.

A less childish and perhaps more formal chimney-piece decoration takes the form of two hanging ornaments made to resemble the carved decorations one sees in eighteenth-century French panelled rooms. The pair shown are made on a flat plaque of leaves; a child's rake and broom crossed, half a high-handled basket in the middle and the whole lightly painted white and heavily glittered. I have in front of me a design for a

hanging drop for a panel, with an open music book, lyre and lute and a chaplet of laurel. This would be entirely charming reproduced in glittered Christmas 'nonsense'. And if this seems too much to attempt you can make simple wall drops of holly.

If holly hanging drops are adopted, the scheme may be completed by fixing a holly wreath on a mirror over the chimney-piece or a holly garland over the length of the mantel. Keep the berries well in evidence, if necessary using the subterfuge I have already described.

Some time ago there was a delightful article in *Country Life* about an old English ornament which we used to call a Kissing Bunch. Particularly elegant variants of this were illustrated, but even in a simple form it is one of the prettiest of Christmas ornaments. It is in the shape of a sphere and is made by intersecting hoops which may be trimmed as you please with evergreen or bound with ribbon. Silver bells or balloons or apples hang inside and on the bottom is a bunch of mistletoe. Last year we bound the hoops with silver paper, hung silver paper bells inside, trimmed the top with evergreen and tied the mistletoe on with cellophane ribbons. These kissing bunches are gay but they have an elegance of form which fits them for formal surroundings. To hang in a window one may use a single small hoop bound in the same way and trimmed at the bottom with a bunch of holly or mistletoe; it can hold a bright bird either of china or modelled out of cellophane or a stuffed one painted. Children love birds but a sensitive child hates the thought of captivity; this is a compromise.

For the chimney-piece of a night nursery a Christmas angel can be made with cellophane, the face painted or pencilled on a scrap of silk. The wings are easily made of cellophane but prettier if made of real feathers, glued on to stiff brown paper and gilded. Such wings make the necessary distinction between angel and fairy, for the wings of the fairy queen are best made of cellophane.

The fairy queen, the crowning glory of the Christmas tree, should be delicate enough, glittering enough, extravagantly fairy-like enough, to call forth that blissful childish sigh. She may be a positive extravaganza of a fairy queen. Her petticoats may billow and glitter, her crown be as high and fantastic as you like and her wand as delicate as though it were made of glass—and all with a few sheets or a reel of cellophane and a little Christmas glitter. . . .

But first the tree. It is unwise to depart too far from tradition where children are concerned and so the fir tree must take its annual place, but, if in an expensive and enthusiastic mood you add a *fairy* tree, you will probably not regret the extra effort. A delicate bare tree, birch perhaps, or a big branch of damson or wild plum fixed in a pot to look like a growing tree is lightly whitened and glittered. If it is trimmed at all, this should be done delicately; cellophane tassels and butterflies and cobwebs of silver wire and little lanterns of plaited cellophane —perhaps a glittered white bird, but everything fairylike, shimmering. Set such a tree in an alcove, floodlight it; leave the rest of the room in shadow and you have something dramatic and lovely which appeals to any child.

In the name of gaiety, conventional trees are sometimes made almost ugly by overcrowding and a vague idea that 'anything goes'. The best effects are generally obtained by adhering to a colour scheme rather than allowing a jumble of colour. The lower branches often need to be weighted to make them take a graceful shape; horse chestnuts wrapped in metal paper and then tied in cellophane, or cones wired, are easy to fasten on and will do the trick. You may increase the appearance of symmetry, important in a Christmas tree, by plaiting ropes of cellophane and winding them spirally down the tree, attaching the plaits here and there to a suitable branch tip. At these points you may attach cellophane tassels or imitation candles or lanterns. Whether you decide to risk real candles or to play for safety with a floodlight you will want some suggestion of candles or lanterns. A simple method of making these is described later.

If you decide on brilliant trimmings, make them really brilliant; this is best done by using strong coloured paint over white. A glittering tree decorated with magenta trimmings is lovely and not at all gaudy.

It is disappointing to a child to see a gay-looking tree and to find on closer inspection that the individual decorations have no particular charm. Since we have not had for so long the enchanting glass toys that came from the Continent we have had to make what we can—and, without any intention of dictating, I should like to say that I am against the introduction of the comic or grotesque in these toys. I like them to be lighthearted, gay, pretty, even beautiful—as they can be—but not, in the name of childhood, funny. I will admit prejudice in this: my first pantomime was *Cinderella*. I was madly excited at the thought of so delicate a spectacle and sadly disappointed at the introduction of the grotesque. This perhaps has narrowed my taste.

Here is a list, planned to appeal to a child's fancy, of toys that can be made with such materials as are available—cellophane is the basis of most of these suggestions: a fairy queen of cellophane and silver; Red Riding Hood with cloak of painted cellophane; elves and gnomes in green with high hats with plumes; cellophane baskets filled with painted 'fruits' and flowers; witches on broomsticks; tinsel flower pictures made with narrow silver metal strips called radar tape which is available now; bird cages of cellophane-covered wire with robins or a modelled bird inside; angels made from silver or gold paper (the formality of these makes them suitable for a Christmas tree in a church);

round posies of paper flowers surrounded by glittered paper doilies tied with painted cellophane ribbons; tassels of finely cut cellophane or radar tape; pompoms of radar tape; fans of silver or gold with cellophane bows; minute candelabra with cake candles; painted and glittered fir cones to weight the tree branches.

Perhaps the last paragraph emphasizes the thought expressed at the beginning of these notes—the need to summon childhood's memories, to let the fancy roam—to play again. When the work table is covered with cellophane and paint and wire and scissors I am back again in that recurring childhood dream where I found myself in a wonderful toy shop with freedom to choose whatever I liked. This time I don't leave the thrill behind with sleep for I am there and can have whatever I like!

2

Fancies into Fact

IVEN A LITTLE patience and a modicum of ingenuity, you need have no difficulty in contriving any of the decorations and toys I have described. The following notes should enable even those with no previous experience to produce effective and workmanlike results.

For frosting or glittering seedheads and twigs for the table centre, you will need suitable seedheads such as wild parsnip or angelica or carrot—any umbrella-shaped head will serve together with spikes of such plants as delphinium or evening primrose seed—while corky elm or delicate birch or twiggy wild plum are good for the twigs.

Take artists gum or dissolve gum arabic in cold water (this takes some time to dissolve so make it a day or two before it is required), brush the twigs over thinly and sprinkle with bought glitter or Epsom salts. If the gum is too thick and too wet the coating will be heavy. Allow to dry completely before use or the 'frost' may get damaged. A touch of white paint here and there before glittering gives a whiter effect but is less natural looking.

Ivy leaves look best rimmed fairly heavily and veined lightly with frost; the stems can be treated solidly or left green. The gourds and cones can be painted first, perhaps in different colours, and the glitter can be put straight on to the paint while it is still tacky.

For wire-netting the containers, choose one of big mesh and thin wire. Crumple it up and press it into the container; for a shallow tray or dish, shape it in a mound, tie it in with string over and across the whole like a parcel. Press it down a little to make a hollow for the gourds. Make a fringe of leaves to hide the wire and pile up the gourds and cones. A little glue dropped from a stick between these will hold them so that if you wish you can build high.

124

To cover a basket with cellophane, take a reel of cellophane and crush it lengthwise so that it is solid and ropy. Start at the bottom and, as you bind, take strips of gummed cellophane tape from under the bottom of the basket over the roped cellophane. You will find that with very little application of the gummed tape the cellophane rope will stay in place. Bind the handle in the same way. For the little baskets you need no frame. Wrap the roped cellophane round the tip of two fingers and go on winding till you have made a sort of bird's-nest shape. Keep in place with strips of cellophane tape taken from one edge of the basket to the other, outside and over the base; make a handle of wire bound with a strip of narrow cellophane and finish with tassels or bows of cellophane. The 'fruit' for these is made of painted horse chestnuts and bunches of ' grapes ' made of acorns. These may be wired together or, more simply, twisted in cellophane and tied together, as boiled sweets used to be tied, in bunches.

Making the synthetic snow scene is the greatest fun and gives infinite scope for imagination and fancy. No sooner was this one made, than another was started, this time of Cinderella and her coach, drawn by mice and accompanied by fairy godmother, witch on broomstick flying away and all the rest of it!

A sheet of glass is a good basis because one gets a better sense of perspective. The sky (blue paper or paint) goes behind the glass and so does the blue lake. The rest of the picture is made on the front of the glass. Peaked mountains are cut out of sheet cotton wool and gummed on; fir trees are cut out of green paper (the branches glittered) and gummed over the cotton wool. The castle is cut out of brown paper and glittered and red sequins make glowing windows. The cascade is made of radar tape and cellophane. The body of the sleigh is cut out of bright red paper, the runners out of gold and the horse of silver, with drapings of colour and plumes of red ostrich feather. The lady stands out three dimensionally, for her head and shoulders are constructed like those of the dolls described below, and her flowing cape is of red painted cellophane and cotton wool fur. The whole is framed with gummed paper.

To make the wall drops, cut a piece of wire netting the shape and size you want. A good oval is probably most satisfactory. Cover this

with moss which you tie in place with string taken over and over. Fasten laurel leaves all over the surface either by sewing them on or with hairpins, or wires bent double. Fix the ornament—rake and broom, spade and fork, toy musical instrument or what you choose— at a pleasing angle and crossing each other, then cover the join with the half basket. The 'trophies' can all be secured with wire or string taken through the plaque and tied at the back. Brush lightly with paint if possible or with distemper—the latter is inclined to chip off but will stand reasonable treatment. If paint is used, the glitter may be put on while it is tacky; if distemper, this should dry well, then be coated with gum and glittered. The whole thing should hang with long ribbons, cord or thin rope.

Effective imitation candles are made like this: take a length of strong, rough packing string. Fray out a wick. Lay the string on a table and roll it in newspaper until it is as thick as a candle. Finish with white paper, leaving the wick exposed at the top. Paint this bright scarlet or gold, and glitter the whole. Kept to a moderate length these 'candles' are easily fastened to the tree by binding the bottom of the candle to a branch with wire. Better still, set them in a 'lantern' made of two hoops of cellophane-covered wire—the two hoops may also be made of willow twigs whitened and frosted.

The dolls are not difficult to make and as they can be varied in so many ways are worth mastering. The head may be made over an acorn or a little ball of cotton wool. Roll the wool between your palms and make it firm; stretch a scrap of thin silk over it and indicate a face either with pencil or brush. Take a stiff wire to hold the arms and clothes, fasten the head on to it by sticking the wire into the wool and binding the base with a bit of fine wire or thread. Now take strip cellophane, tightly crush it; and bind round the head to make a halo-like head-dress. Take a piece of wire long enough for both arms, bind it tightly with narrow cellophane, then make sleeves of uncrushed cellophane, tying at the wrists to form a little frill to suggest hands. Fasten this across the main wire high up, leaving only a little space for the neck. Cut a circle of white or coloured paper and slip over the main wire to form a first petticoat—it should come to the bottom of the wire or beyond. Now make covering petticoats of cellophane either with sheets or with loops from the reel cellophane. On the final petticoat paint a design—stars, lines, scallops, what you will, with gold paint, and sprinkle with glitter while the paint is tacky. Fasten these securely at the waist with wire, preferably a piece of fairly strong reel wire. Put it round twice and then twist the ends with pliers, pulling as you do so, in order to obtain a good firm grip. The next step is to crush reel cellophane into a rope and bind over the shoulders and round the waist and fasten with gummed cellophane. Make the petticoats bouffant and the bodice tight. On this basis you can make angels, fairy queens and a variety of figures. Thus, for Red Riding Hood, you paint the cellophane underneath with bright red oil colour and edge the cloak with wisps of cotton wool fastened with gum.

A snow queen pleases children. For this, use a folded sheet of cellophane for the top petticoat and lay a sheet of cotton wool between the cellophane. Then gum ' snow flakes ' all over it. Do the same for her cloak. For the bonnet, use a folded piece of cellophane lined and trimmed with cotton wool. Give her a cotton wool muff and a posy of small holly.

The fairy queen needs a high, glittering crown which is made of paper, glittered and pinned through the cellophane binding on the head.

Her wand is of cellophane-bound wire with a tinsel star on the tip, her wings a large cellophane bow.

These dolls all have petticoats to the ground and stand on their petticoats. For ballet dancers one uses cellophane bound wires which need to be more carefully bound and shaped, and then the petticoats are cut in circles in many layers like a pen wiper, and crushed a little when finished to make them stand apart.

The formal angels are started in the same way as the dolls but their dresses and wings are cut out of gold or silver paper and made to look as stately as possible. In every case it is wise, unless you are very skilled, merely to indicate the face and not to paint in too much detail.

Christmas reading

There is a skeleton in every house

A good tale is none the worse for being twice told

It would vex a dog to see a pudding creep

The Yellow Wall-paper

BY CHARLOTTE PERKINS GILMAN

Although first published over half a century ago, and by a well-known American writer, this curious story has not turned up in the ghost anthologies with the tedious regularity of many others of much less calibre. Partly for this reason it is printed here and partly because, read aloud, preferably by a woman, it makes a highly satisfactory creepy *fireside tale.*

T IS VERY seldom that mere ordinary people like John and myself secure ancestral halls for the summer.

A colonial mansion, a hereditary estate, I would say a haunted house, and reach the height of romantic felicity—but that would be asking too much of fate!

Still I will proudly declare that there is something queer about it.

Else, why should it be let so cheaply? And why have stood so long untenanted?

John laughs at me, of course, but one expects that in marriage.

John is practical in the extreme. He has no patience with faith, an intense horror of superstition, and he scoffs openly at any talk of things not to be felt and seen and put down in figures.

John is a physician, and *perhaps*—(I would not say it to a living soul, of course, but this is dead paper and a great relief to my mind)—*perhaps* that is one reason I do not get well faster.

You see, he does not believe I am sick!

And what can one do?

If a physician of high standing, and one's own husband, assures friends and relatives that there is really nothing the matter with one but temporary nervous depression—a slight hysterical tendency—what is one to do?

My brother is also a physician, and also of high standing, and he says the same thing.

So I take phosphates or phosphites—whichever it is—and tonics, and journeys, and air, and exercise, and am absolutely forbidden to 'work' until I am well again.

Personally I disagree with their ideas.

Personally I believe that congenial work, with excitement and change, would do me good.

But what is one to do?

I did write for a while in spite of them; but it *does* exhaust me a good deal—having to be so sly about it, or else meet with heavy opposition.

I sometimes fancy that in my condition if I had less opposition and more society and stimulus—but John says the very worst thing I can do is to think about my condition, and I confess it always makes me feel bad.

So I will let it alone and talk about the house.

The most beautiful place! It is quite alone, standing well back from the road, quite three miles from the village. It makes me think of English places that you read about, for there are hedges, and walls and gates that lock, and lots of separate little houses for the gardeners and people.

There is a *delicious* garden! I never saw such a garden—large and shady, full of box-bordered paths, and lined with long grape-covered arbours with seats under them.

There were greenhouses, too, but they are all broken now.

There was some legal trouble, I believe, something about the heirs and co-heirs; anyhow, the place has been empty for years.

That spoils my ghostliness, I am afraid; but I don't care—there is something strange about the house—I can feel it.

I even said so to John one moonlit evening, but he said what I felt was a *draught*, and shut the window.

I get unreasonably angry with John sometimes. I'm sure I never used to be so sensitive. I think it is due to this nervous condition.

But John says if I feel so I shall neglect proper self-control; so I take pains to control myself—before him, at least, and that makes me very tired.

I don't like our room a bit. I wanted one downstairs that opened on the piazza and had roses all over the window, and such pretty, old-fashioned chintz hangings! but John would not hear of it.

He said there was only one window and not room for two beds, and no near room for him if he took another.

He is very careful and loving, and hardly lets me stir without special direction.

I have a schedule prescription for each hour in the day; he takes all care from me, and so I feel basely ungrateful not to value it more.

He said we came here solely on my account, that I was to have perfect rest and all the air I could get. ' Your exercise depends on your strength, my dear,' said he, ' and your food somewhat on your appetite; but air you can absorb all the time.' So we took the nursery at the top of the house.

It is a big, airy room, the whole floor nearly, with windows that look all ways, and air and sunshine galore. It was nursery first and then playground and gymnasium, I should judge; for the windows are barred for little children, and there are rings and things in the walls.

The paint and paper look as if a boys' school had used it. It is stripped off—the paper—in great patches all around the head of my bed, about as far as I can reach, and in a great place on the other side of the room, low down. I never saw a worse paper in my life.

One of those sprawling, flamboyant patterns committing every artistic sin.

It is dull enough to confuse the eye in following, pronounced enough to constantly irritate, and provoke study, and when you follow the lame, uncertain curves for a little distance they suddenly commit suicide— plunge off at outrageous angles, destroy themselves in unheard-of contradictions.

The colour is repellent, almost revolting; a smouldering, unclean yellow, strangely faded by the low turning sunlight.

It is a dull yet lurid orange in some places, a sickly sulphur tint in others.

No wonder the children hated it! I should hate it myself if I had to live in this room long.

There comes John, and I must put this away—he hates to have me write a word.

We have been here two weeks, and I haven't felt like writing before, since that first day.

I am sitting by the window now, up in this atrocious nursery, and there is nothing to hinder my writing as I please, save lack of strength.

John is away all day, and even some nights when his cases are serious.

I am glad my case is not serious!

But these nervous troubles are dreadfully depressing.

John does not know how much I really suffer. He knows there is no *reason* to suffer, and that satisfies him.

Of course it is only nervousness. It does weigh on me so not to do my duty in any way!

I meant to be such a help to John, such a real rest and comfort, and here I am a comparative burden already!

Nobody would believe what an effort it is to do what little I am able— to dress and entertain, and order things.

It is fortunate Mary is so good with the baby. Such a dear baby!

And yet I *cannot* be with him, it makes me so nervous.

I suppose John never was nervous in his life. He laughs at me so about this wall-paper!

At first he meant to re-paper the room, but afterwards he said that I was letting it get the better of me, and that nothing was worse for a nervous patient than to give way to such fancies.

He said that after the wall-paper was changed it would be the heavy bedstead, and then the barred windows, and then that gate at the head of the stairs, and so on.

'You know the place is doing you good,' he said, 'and really, dear, I don't care to renovate the house just for a three months' rental.'

'Then do let us go downstairs,' I said, 'there are such pretty rooms there.'

Then he took me in his arms and called me a blessed little goose, and said he would go down in the cellar if I wished, and would have it white-washed into the bargain.

But he is right enough about the beds and windows and things.

It is as airy and comfortable a room as any one need wish, and, of course, I would not be so silly as to make him uncomfortable just for a whim.

I'm really getting quite fond of the big room, all but that horrid paper.

Out of one window I can see the garden, those mysterious deep-shaded arbours, the riotous old-fashioned flowers, and bushes and gnarly trees.

Out of another I get a lovely view of the bay and a little private wharf belonging to the estate. There is a beautiful shaded lane that runs down there from the house. I always fancy I see people walking in these numerous paths and arbours, but John has cautioned me not to give way to fancy in the least. He says that with my imaginative power and habit of story-making a nervous weakness like mine is sure to lead to all manner of excited fancies, and that I ought to use my will and good sense to check the tendency. So I try.

I think sometimes that if I were only well enough to write a little it would relieve the press of ideas and rest me.

But I find I get pretty tired when I try.

It is so discouraging not to have any advice and companionship about my work. When I get really well John says we will ask Cousin Henry and Julia down for a long visit; but he says he would as soon put fireworks in my pillowcase as to let me have those stimulating people about now.

I wish I could get well faster.

But I must not think about that. This paper looks to me as if it *knew* what a vicious influence it had!

There is a recurrent spot where the pattern lolls like a broken neck and two bulbous eyes stare at you upside-down.

I got positively angry with the impertinence of it and the ever-lastingness. Up and down and sideways they crawl, and those absurd, unblinking eyes are everywhere. There is one place where two breadths didn't match, and the eyes go all up and down the line, one a little higher than the other.

I never saw so much expression in an inanimate thing before, and we all know how much expression they have!

I used to lie awake as a child and get more entertainment and terror out of blank walls and plain furniture than most children could find in a toy-store.

I remember what a kindly wink the knobs of our big old bureau used to have, and there was one chair that always seemed like a strong friend.

I used to feel that if any of the other things looked too fierce I could always hop into that chair and be safe.

The furniture in this room is no worse than inharmonious, however, for we had to bring it all from downstairs. I suppose when this was used as a playroom they had to take the nursery things out, and no wonder! I never saw such ravages as the children have made here.

The wall-paper, as I said before, is torn off in spots, and it sticketh closer than a brother—they must have had perseverance as well as hatred.

Then the floor is scratched and gouged and splintered, the plaster itself is dug out here and there, and this great heavy bed, which is all we found in the room, looks as if it had been through the wars.

But I don't mind it a bit—only the paper.

There comes John's sister. Such a dear girl as she is, and so careful of me! I must not let her find me writing.

She is a perfect, an enthusiastic housekeeper, and hopes for no better profession. I verily believe she thinks it is the writing which made me sick!

But I can write when she is out, and see her a long way off from these windows.

There is one that commands the road, a lovely, shaded, winding road, and one that just looks off over the country. A lovely country, too, full of great elms and velvet meadows.

This wall-paper has a kind of sub-pattern in a different shade, a particularly irritating one, for you can only see it in certain lights, and not clearly then.

But in the places where it isn't faded, and where the sun is just so, I can see a strange, provoking, formless sort of figure, that seems to sulk about that silly and conspicuous front design.

There's sister on the stairs!

Well, the Fourth of July is over! The people are all gone and I am tired out. John thought it might do me good to see a little company, so we just had Mother and Nellie and the children down for a week.

Of course I didn't do a thing. Jennie sees to everything now.

But it tires me all the same.

John says if I don't pick up faster he shall send me to Weir Mitchell in the fall.

But I don't want to go there at all. I had a friend who was in his hands once, and she says he is just like John and my brother, only more so!

Besides, it is such an undertaking to go so far.

I don't feel as if it was worth while to turn my hand over for anything, and I'm getting dreadfully fretful and querulous.

I cry at nothing, and cry most of the time.

Of course I don't when John is here, or anybody else, but when I am alone.

And I am alone a good deal just now, John is kept in town very often by serious cases, and Jennie is good and lets me alone when I want her to.

So I walk a little in the garden, or down that lovely lane, sit on the porch under the roses, and lie down up here a good deal.

I'm getting really fond of the room in spite of the wall-paper. Perhaps *because* of the wall-paper.

It dwells in my mind so!

I lie here on this great immovable bed—it is nailed down, I believe—and follow that pattern about by the hour. It is as good as gymnastics, I assure you. I start, we'll say, at the bottom, down in the corner over there where it has not been touched, and I determine for the thousandth time that I *will* follow that pointless pattern to some sort of a conclusion.

I know a little of the principles of design, and I know this thing was not arranged on any laws of radiation, or alternation, or repetition, or symmetry, or anything else that I ever heard of.

It is repeated, of course, by the breadths, but not otherwise.

Looked at in one way, each breadth stands alone, the bloated curves and flourishes—a kind of 'debased Romanesque' with *delirium tremens*—go waddling up and down in isolated columns of fatuity.

But, on the other hand, they connect diagonally, and the sprawling outlines run off in great slanting waves of optic horror, like a lot of wallowing seaweeds in full chase.

The whole thing goes horizontally, too, at least it seems so, and I exhaust myself in trying to distinguish the order of its going in that direction.

They have used a horizontal breadth for a frieze, and that adds wonderfully to the confusion.

There is one end of the room where it is almost intact, and there, when the cross-lights fade and the low sun shines directly upon it, I can almost fancy radiation, after all—the interminable grotesques seem to form around a common centre and rush off in headlong plunges of equal distraction.

It makes me tired to follow it. I will take a nap, I guess.

I don't know why I should write this.

I don't want to.

I don't feel able.

And I know John would think it absurd. But I *must* say what I feel and think in some way—it is such a relief!

But the effort is getting to be greater than the relief.

Half the time now I am awfully lazy, and lie down ever so much.

John says I mustn't lose my strength, and has me take cod-liver oil and lots of tonics and things, to say nothing of ale and wine and rare meat.

Dear John! He loves me very dearly, and hates to have me sick. I tried to have a real earnest reasonable talk with him the other day, and tell him how I wished he would let me go and make a visit to Cousin Henry and Julia.

But he said I wasn't able to go, nor able to stand it after I got there; and I did not make out a very good case for myself, for I was crying before I had finished.

It is getting to be a great effort for me to think straight. Just this nervous weakness, I suppose.

And dear John gathered me up in his arms, and just carried me upstairs and laid me on the bed, and sat by me and read to me till he tired my head.

He said I was his darling and his comfort and all he had, and that I must take care of myself for his sake, and keep well.

He says no one but myself can help me out of it, that I must use my will and self-control and not let my silly fancies run away with me.

There's one comfort, the baby is well and happy, and does not have to occupy this nursery with the horrid wall-paper.

If we had not used it that blessed child would have! What a fortunate escape! Why, I wouldn't have a child of mine, an impressionable little thing, live in such a room for worlds.

I never thought of it before, but it is lucky that John kept me here, after all. I can stand it so much easier than a baby, you see.

Of course I never mention it to them any more—I am too wise—

but I keep watch of it all the same. There are things in that paper that nobody knows but me, or ever will.

Behind that outside pattern the dim shapes get clearer every day.

It is always the same shape, only very numerous.

And it is like a woman stooping down and creeping about behind that pattern. I don't like it a bit. I wonder—I begin to think—I wish John would take me away from here!

It is so hard to talk with John about my case, because he is so wise, and because he loves me so.

But I tried it last night.

It was moonlight. The moon shines in all around, just as the sun does.

I hate to see it sometimes, it creeps so slowly, and always comes in by one window or another.

John was asleep and I hated to waken him, so I kept still and watched the moonlight on that undulating wall-paper till I felt creepy.

The faint figure behind seemed to shake the pattern, just as if she wanted to get out.

I got up softly and went to feel and see if the paper *did* move, and when I came back John was awake.

'What is it, little girl?' he said. 'Don't go walking about like that—you'll get cold.'

I thought it was a good time to talk, so I told him that I really was not gaining here, and that I wished he would take me away.

'Why, darling!' said he, 'our lease will be up in three weeks, and I can't see how to leave before.

'The repairs are not done at home, and I cannot possibly leave town just now. Of course if you were in any danger I could and would, but you really are better, dear, whether you can see it or not. I am a doctor, dear, and I know. You are gaining flesh and colour, your appetite is better. I feel really much easier about you.'

'I don't weigh a bit more,' said I, 'nor as much; and my appetite may be better in the evening, when you are here, but it is worse in the morning, when you are away.'

'Bless her little heart!' said he with a big hug; 'she shall be as sick as she pleases. But now let's improve the shining hours by going to sleep, and talk about it in the morning.'

138

' And you won't go away? ' I asked gloomily.

' Why, how can I, dear? It is only three weeks more and then we will take a nice little trip for a few days while Jennie is getting the house ready. Really, dear, you are better! '

' Better in body, perhaps—— ' I began, and stopped short, for he sat up straight and looked at me with such a stern, reproachful look that I could not say another word.

' My darling,' said he, ' I beg of you, for my sake and for our child's sake, as well as for your own, that you will never for one instant let that idea enter your mind! There is nothing so dangerous, so fascinating to a temperament like yours. It is a false and foolish fancy. Can you not trust me as a physician when I tell you so? '

So of course I said no more on that score, and we went to sleep before long. He thought I was asleep first, but I wasn't—I lay there for hours trying to decide whether that front pattern and the back pattern really did move together or separately.

On a pattern like this, by daylight, there is a lack of sequence, a defiance of law, that is a constant irritant to a normal mind.

The colour is hideous enough, and unreliable enough, and infuriating enough, but the pattern is torturing.

You think you have mastered it, but just as you get well under way in following, it turns a back somersault, and there you are. It slaps you in the face, knocks you down, and tramples upon you. It is like a bad dream.

The outside pattern is a florid arabesque, reminding one of a fungus. If you can imagine a toadstool in joints, an interminable string of toad-stools, budding and sprouting in endless convolutions—why, that is something like it.

That is, sometimes!

There is one marked peculiarity about this paper, a thing nobody seems to notice but myself, and that is that it changes as the light changes.

When the sun shoots in through the east window—I always watch for that first long, straight ray—it changes so quickly that I never can quite believe it.

That is why I watch it always.

By moonlight—the moon shines in all night when there is a moon—I wouldn't know it was the same paper.

At night in any kind of light, in twilight, candlelight, lamplight, and worst of all by moonlight, it becomes bars! The outside pattern, I mean, and the woman behind it is as plain as can be.

I didn't realise for a long time what the thing was that showed behind—that dim sub-pattern—but now I am quite sure it is a woman.

By daylight she is subdued, quiet. I fancy it is the pattern that keeps her so still. It is so puzzling. It keeps me quiet by the hour.

I lie down ever so much now. John says it is good for me, and to sleep all I can.

Indeed, he started the habit by making me lie down for an hour after each meal.

It is a very bad habit, I am convinced, for, you see, I don't sleep.

And that cultivates deceit, for I don't tell them I'm awake—oh, no! The fact is, I am getting a little afraid of John.

He seems very queer sometimes, and even Jennie has an inexplicable look.

It strikes me occasionally, just as a scientific hypothesis, that perhaps it is the paper!

I have watched John when he did not know I was looking, and come into the room suddenly on the most innocent excuses, and I've caught him several times *looking at the paper*! And Jennie, too. I caught Jennie with her hand on it once.

She didn't know I was in the room, and when I asked her in a quiet, a very quiet voice, with the most restrained manner possible, what she was doing with the paper she turned around as if she had been caught stealing, and looked quite angry—asked me why I should frighten her so!

Then she said that the paper stained everything it touched, and that she had found yellow smooches on all my clothes and John's, and she wished we would be more careful!

Did not that sound innocent? But I know she was studying that pattern, and I am determined that nobody shall find it out but myself!

Life is very much more exciting now than it used to be. You see I have something more to expect, to look forward to, to watch. I really do eat better, and am more quiet than I was.

John is so pleased to see me improve! He laughed a little the other day, and said I seemed to be flourishing in spite of my wall-paper.

I turned it off with a laugh. I had no intention of telling him that it was *because* of the wall-paper—he would make fun of me. He might even want to take me away.

I don't want to leave now until I have found it out. There is a week more, and I think that will be enough.

I'm feeling ever so much better! I don't sleep much at night, for it is so interesting to watch developments; but I sleep a good deal in the daytime.

In the daytime it is tiresome and perplexing.

There are always new shoots on the fungus, and new shades of yellow all over it. I cannot keep count of them, though I have tried conscientiously.

It is the strangest yellow, that wall-paper! It makes me think of all the yellow things I ever saw—not beautiful ones like buttercups, but old foul, bad yellow things.

But there is something else about that paper—the smell! I noticed it the moment we came into the room, but with so much air and sun it was not too bad. Now we have had a week of fog and rain, and whether the windows are open or not the smell is here.

It creeps all over the house.

I find it hovering in the dining-room, skulking in the parlour, hiding in the hall, lying in wait for me on the stairs.

It gets into my hair.

Even when I go to ride, if I turn my head suddenly and surprise it—there is that smell!

Such a peculiar odour, too! I have spent hours in trying to analyse it, to find what it smelled like.

It is not bad—at first, and very gentle, but quite the subtlest, most enduring odour I ever met.

In this damp weather it is awful. I wake up in the night and find it hanging over me.

It used to disturb me at first. I thought seriously of burning the house—to reach the smell.

But now I am used to it. The only thing I can think of that it is like is the *colour* of the paper—a yellow smell!

There is a very funny mark on this wall, low down, near the mop-board. A streak that runs around the room. It goes behind every piece of furniture, except the bed, a long, straight, even *smooch*, as if it had been rubbed over and over.

I wonder how it was done and who did it, and what they did it for. Round and round and round—round and round and round—it makes me dizzy.

I really have discovered something at last.

Through watching so much at night, when it changes so, I have finally found out.

The front pattern *does* move—and no wonder! The woman behind shakes it!

Sometimes I think there are a great many women behind, and sometimes only one, and she crawls around fast, and her crawling shakes it all over.

Then in the very bright spots she keeps still, and in the very shady spots she just takes hold of the bars and shakes them hard.

And she is all the time trying to climb through. But nobody could climb through that pattern—it strangles so; I think that is why it has so many heads.

They get through, and then the pattern strangles them off and turns them upside-down, and makes their eyes white!

If those heads were covered or taken off it would not be half so bad.

I think that woman gets out in the daytime!

And I'll tell you why—privately—I've seen her!

I can see her out of every one of my windows!

It is the same woman, I know, for she is always creeping, and most women do not creep by daylight.

I see her in that long shaded lane, creeping up and down. I see her in those dark grape arbours, creeping all around the garden.

I see her on that long road under the trees, creeping along, and when a carriage comes she hides under the blackberry vines.

I don't blame her a bit. It must be very humiliating to be caught creeping by daylight!

I always lock the door when I creep by daylight. I can't do it at night, for I know John would suspect something at once.

And John is so queer, now, that I don't want to irritate him. I wish he would take another room! Besides, I don't want anybody to get that woman out at night but myself.

I often wonder if I could see her out of all the windows at once.

But, turn as fast as I can, I can only see out of one at one time.

And though I always see her she *may* be able to creep faster than I can turn!

I have watched her sometimes away off in the open country, creeping as fast as a cloud shadow in a high wind.

If only that top pattern could be gotten off from the under one! I mean to try it, little by little.

I have found out another funny thing, but I shan't tell it this time! It does not do to trust people too much.

There are only two more days to get this paper off, and I believe John is beginning to notice. I don't like the look in his eyes.

And I heard him ask Jennie a lot of professional questions about me. She had a very good report to give.

She said I slept a good deal in the daytime.

John knows I don't sleep very well at night, for all I'm so quiet!

He asked me all sorts of questions, too, and pretended to be very loving and kind.

As if I couldn't see through him!

Still, I don't wonder he acts so, sleeping under this paper for three months.

It only interests me, but I feel sure John and Jennie are secretly affected by it.

Hurrah! This is the last day, but it is enough. John is to stay in town over night, and won't be out until this evening.

Jennie wanted to sleep with me—the sly thing!—but I told her I should undoubtedly rest better for a night all alone.

That was clever, for really I wasn't alone a bit! As soon as it was moonlight, and that poor thing began to crawl and shake the pattern, I got up and ran to help her.

I pulled and she shook, I shook and she pulled, and before morning we had peeled off yards of that paper.

A strip about as high as my head and half around the room.

And then when the sun came and that awful pattern began to laugh at me I declared I would finish it today!

We go away tomorrow, and they are moving all my furniture down again to leave things as they were before.

Jennie looked at the wall in amazement, but I told her merrily that I did it out of pure spite at the vicious thing.

She laughed and said she wouldn't mind doing it herself, but I must not get tired.

How she betrayed herself that time!

But I am here, and no person touches this paper but me—not *alive*!

She tried to get me out of the room—it was too patent! But I said it was so quiet and empty and clean now that I believed I would lie down again and sleep all I could; and not to wake me even for dinner— I would call when I woke.

So now she is gone, and the servants are gone, and the things are gone, and there is nothing left but that great bedstead nailed down, with the canvas mattress we found on it.

We shall sleep downstairs tonight, and take the boat home tomorrow.

I quite enjoy the room, now it is bare again.

How those children did tear about here!

This bedstead is fairly gnawed!

But I must get to work.

I have locked the door and thrown the key down into the front path.

I don't want to go out, and I don't want to have anybody come in, till John comes.

I want to astonish him.

I've got a rope up here that even Jennie did not find. If that woman does get out, and tries to get away, I can tie her!

But I forgot I could not reach far without anything to stand on!

This bed will *not* move!

I tried to lift and push it until I was lame, and then I got so angry I bit off a little piece at one corner—but it hurt my teeth.

Then I peeled off all the paper I could reach standing on the floor. It sticks horribly and the pattern just enjoys it! All these strangled heads and bulbous eyes and waddling fungus growths just shriek with derision!

I am getting angry enough to do something desperate. To jump out of the window would be admirable exercise, but the bars are too strong even to try.

Besides, I wouldn't do it. Of course not. I know well enough that a step like that is improper and might be misconstrued.

I don't like to *look* out of the windows even—there are so many of those creeping women, and they creep so fast.

I wonder if they all come out of that wall-paper, as I did?

But I am securely fastened now by my well-hidden rope—you don't get *me* out in the road there!

I suppose I shall have to get back behind the pattern when it comes night, and that is hard!

It is so pleasant to be out in this great room and creep around as I please!

I don't want to go outside. I won't, even if Jennie asks me to.

For outside you have to creep on the ground, and everything is green instead of yellow.

But here I can creep smoothly on the floor, and my shoulder just fits in that long smooch around the wall, so I cannot lose my way.

145

Why, there's John at the door!

It is no use, young man, you can't open it!

How he does call and pound!

Now he's crying for an axe.

It would be a shame to break down that beautiful door!

'John, dear,' said I in the gentlest voice, 'the key is down by the front steps, under a plantain leaf!'

That silenced him for a few moments.

Then he said—very quietly indeed, 'Open the door, my darling !'

'I can't,' said I. 'The key is down by the front door, under a plantain leaf!'

And then I said it again, several times, very gently and slowly, and said it so often that he had to go and see, and he got it, of course, and came in. He stopped short by the door.

'What is the matter?' he cried. 'For God's sake, what are you doing?'

I kept on creeping just the same, but I looked at him over my shoulder.

'I've got out at last,' said I, 'in spite of you and Jennie! And I've pulled off most of the paper, so you can't put me back!'

Now why should that man have fainted? But he did, and right across my path by the wall, so that I had to creep over him every time!

Murder

BY WILLIAM SANSOM

A BUZZ AT THE DOOR, one, shorter than the postman's, shy as the finger-push of a visitor who feels his visit has no right. Neal, approaching the door, peered uncertainly at the shape unfocused behind the frosted glass; certainly this visitor was a short one, short as his timid buzz. He opened the door. There stood a man he had never seen before.

Moreover, this short strange man was leaning his head forwards, standing with his feet close together, smiling. He wore a round snub-peaked cap of unusual design, an informal uniform of slack pale brown material; from his hand hung a canvas bag like a large quiver, and from this there stuck out the ends of a set of dark, metallic rods. Nor did his next behaviour relieve Neal's first small sense of perturbation—for now the stranger made no more attempt to introduce himself, but stood simply quiet and smiling, pushing his face upwards and staring with almost, it seemed, love for Neal. For some seconds they stood thus facing one another.

In this silence, which grew to be uneasily intimate, Neal found that he was observing with disquietening clarity each configuration of the stranger's face, as though it were the face in a particularly clear engraving. This may have been occasioned not only by the silence, nor by the unease of such an encounter, nor even by the features themselves, so large, so grossly defined in a head too big for that small body—but also by the fact that there was snow upon the ground. The snow, now thawing in bright sunlight, refracted a cold light from the ground and thence from the pale house wall, a flood of bright light thus in all directions; it brought into abrupt definition the brown figure sharp against the white yard, yet at the same time flooded the face and front of this stranger with its cold, clinical, reflected light. Neal saw thus the features of a man of thirty, heavy yet in many ways feminine, as though perhaps in his boyhood this face had been a girl's, yet had now become expanded and grossened by an access of repressed male secretions. The pale eyes were thickly lashed, and dreamed from beneath heavily fleshed lids. The mouth cut too largely across cheeks whose dimples seemed to occur then somewhere by the ears—this was an over-formed mouth, baroque-lipped, pink, revealing at each farthest corner two rows of small and absolutely regular teeth. The mouth of a mastodon cupid. The eyes of a whore. Altogether the face, over its blue hair-growth shaved smooth, of an actor rouged and kohled—yet with such exaggerations and colours richly faded and grown into the tegument of the face itself.

All this Neal saw engraved round a certain smiled seduction dreaming up in that white light, with the sun sparkling on the thaw-points dripping round; then suddenly the stranger spoke, apologetically, as though he should never have arrived, though arrived as he was he loved it. He said: ' Sweep, sir.'

A voice so soft. Neal smiled: ' Of course.' And instantly the scene behind, the snow and the thaw and the cause of so much cold light became recognisable: Neal was soon thinking, as he ushered the sweep inside, that of course there had been neither mystery nor unease in that encountered pause, that only such a strangely vivid light had electrified the man's figure into a harder and franker reality than would normally have been perceived: the meeting had never been unreal, it had merely been too real.

In the shade of the hallway the sweep looked like a quite normal small man, with a head too big but in no way cretinous, with a markedly obsequious manner that was hardly unusual, with a smile slow and pleasant but in the soft sense weak.

Neal called through to his wife.

The sweep stood waiting, half bowed, with his feet still close together—a dummy man. Then Elsa came hurrying out from the bedroom, her arms laden with sheets, her head poking above them, her lips saying many things at once. It had been one of those mornings set aside for accumulated odd jobs, so that perversely they had stayed in bed and breakfasted too long, putting off the businesses in the imagined luxury of a morning containing so many hours—ten o'clock, eleven, twelve offering themselves forward endlessly—yet really munching away the time on their voracious pillows. However, now the sweep had pressed the button for action—and in almost one movement Elsa had gathered up the dust-sheets, shepherded the little sweep into the room with the chimney, closed finally the door. So that Neal stood alone in the hall in a sudden quiet after such a feminine, sheet-flurried whirlwind. The draught-felt on the bottom of the door muffled any sound from the room, stifled absolutely whatever Elsa might be saying to the sweep. Provoked by the silence, Neal walked into the room next door, a small empty room where he was painting a chair.

The chair islanded on its carpet of newspaper made absolute the vacuum of four undecorated unfurnished walls. It was anyhow a box of a room, once a china closet among the kitchens of the huge old house and now a spare bedroom in Neal's flat. There was one window, and this looked out on to the level garden. Through this the full illumination of the snow now shone, flooding the ceiling corners white, purifying every inch of the floor, walls and ceiling in shadowless bright light. The smell of paint increased the feeling of a room untenanted, exorcising all other faint smells of dust and use. No sound came through the wall from the other room. Only from outside the thaw dripped, regularly, dripping light long drops as from an immense liquid chandelier depending from the bright sun somewhere over all outside. In such a vacuum, in such a silence full of mineral sound, Neal bent down to his brushes, squeezed out the water, dipped them in the oiled cream and began to paint.

For a time submerged in his task he forgot about the sweep, Elsa, the next room. With long sensuous strokes he smoothed a patina of paint down the chairlegs, then etched with fussing dabs the corners and underneath; only once the whole flat surface of the seat welcomed a smearing of wide easy strokes, when the paint settled down within itself to a most satisfactory square of liquid cream. Through his absorption, Neal became conscious now and again of one faint sound, muffled and distant, from the next-door room—the rattle of the sweep's sticks.

Presently, irritated by an endless recurrence of unforeseen unpainted leg-backs, his fingers gloved with quick-drying paint where he had gripped what he had already painted—he stood up. It was time, even after ten minutes, for a breathing space. His back seemed to curve with ache. He straightened upright and found himself facing the window. Outside there stood, surprisingly, a snowman. A second later he remembered that of course a snowman should have been there— he had built it on the previous day. However, in the change of his eyes from the close focus of the chair to the wide light room and all the breadth of the world in the garden outside, such a white manlike figure still as death proved naturally to be a surprise. So that Neal studied the figure more intently than before, more detachedly, conferring upon it a greater presence of its own. He chuckled, smiled—and then the smile altogether left his lips.

An old fishing cap stood on the snowman's head, a grey scarf hung slack like a drowned squirrel from his neck, a twig stuck out from the lipless mouth to make a sort of cigarette. The snowman looked thus at first sight a figure of fun—with its pinioned arms, its no-legs, its portly helpless tilt. But then—Neal grew conscious of the eyes. In the place for eyes two round black pebbles had been stuck. Now, of all the pale-tinted snow-hung garden, where the trees hung heavy and the alive thaw dripped its deadness on every living thing—the snowman was the only creature that might have moved, that might have had life, that had eyes. These eyes stared. Black eyes, small and ghostly as a gull's. Sockets that had shrunk to a squinting second sight. And since the snowman was placed some yards out on the lawn directly opposite the division between the two rooms it would thus have been able to see into both windows.

Whether it was this omniscient stance or whether the newspapers on the floor—with their stained print telling old stories of real reported deaths—suggested to Neal a sensation of crime, or whether it was

probably both . . . together with the thaw's dripping silence, and the
draughted vacancy of the room . . . however that could be, Neal
suddenly felt the presence of the next-wall room, of its separation, of
the two people enclosed in it alone: and he felt a sense of evil, of the
perpetration of things not right. But—what exactly could not be *right*?
Something against his orders? . . . Nonsense . . . he gave no orders. . . .
Then something opposed to his views of behaviour . . . again what?. . .
He had few such views, except on some violences, some extreme
familiarities. Such as Elsa flirting with the sweep? He smiled, despite
the snowman, despite not quite wishing to smile. He saw Elsa's house-
coat falling back from her leg, saw the intense enquiry in her eyes as
they lit—as always—to see whether her attractions were properly
received. So—then the sweep would kindle; smothering her with his
soot he would embrace her, kiss her with his sweep's lips, do her in;
then what? . . . Sever her head with his scoop? Stuff it up the chimney? Stuff it in the soot bag? . . . Neal laughed aloud, so that the
empty walls rang back the laugh which then sounded as absurd and
delighted as his imagining. Impatiently he turned back to the chair.

Nevertheless, some negative sense persisted, slightly, deeply—a
spiral of unease drifting behind his other thoughts. It was the same
feeling, he remembered suddenly, as when he had returned once to
find the flat burgled. Then also there had not been much to complain
about. Only a broken window, a few oddments taken in a hurry. But
cupboards were open, a suitcase had been moved, drawers were not
shut as they should have been . . . there was a dark sensation, a
whisper, a veil of ancient dread along the passages and round corners,
behind doors and in every room, a whisper not of violence nor of attack
but more a sense of privacy invaded that translated itself into words
repeated and repeated in his ear, softly, as though from the reaches
of very distant years, the deep and hollow warning voice from a fairy-
tale: ' Someone has been here,' the whisper groaned, as it hovered
over each possessive corner of his house, 'someone had been
here. . . .'

Irritated, over-fancying, he turned abruptly back to his work. The
brush was sticking to a piece of newspaper. He tore it off. The paper
stuck to his fingers. A line of paint fell in a thread like white treacle
down to spot his shoe. He swore, turned the chair upside down to paint
the underneath; but then the top, newly-painted, began to stick to the

paper. At the same time, he saw that a quarter-inch rim round the base of each leg had yet to be covered. If that was painted, then reversed, each stump of chair leg would stick to the paper too . . . the whole affair seemed absurdly difficult with only the most tedious resource, that of leaving it to dry and starting all over again to paint at some other time . . . he got up again, and, suddenly tired, abandoned the chair altogether.

Walking with the paint-pot in his hand, he crossed to the wall and began to edge the brush along the wooden dado rail. In silence he worked for some minutes. Sometimes, as he edged along, his shoes shuffled on the boards, sounding a resonance from underneath, echoing like a sudden cough in the stillness. Conscious then of the depth of the quiet of the immobility of the air in that white room, of the snow's reflection on the white plaster, of the disquietening purity of such an acrid paint-poisoned virgin silence glassed and ticking with the outside drip, drip, drip—Neal began to whistle. He whistled two bars of a popular tune, then as abruptly stopped. Absorbed in his brush, the tune has struck his ears impersonally, as from another agent but his own lips, violently human in such a painted silence. He stopped whistling, self-conscious. The silence dropped again like a stone weight. The paintbrush smoothed along quietly, with no sound whatsoever, surprisingly quiet even when it gathered into its whiteness a sharp speck of grit. Then Neal suddenly halted the brush—for some reason, not the whistle, not the quiet paintbrush, the silence was different than before. He stared into the wall—with an alertness possible only to a person alone in a room charged with his own solitude. He cocked his head, listened. Then he had it! The one sound, the sound of the rattle of the sweep's stick—this had stopped.

For how long? How long had the rattle not been? . . . As he thought back, it seemed that such a sound must have stopped some time ago. An irregular sound, it could not have suddenly forced a contrast of quiet, like the stopping of a clock. What then . . .? Facing the blank wall, his mind flashed sideways towards the snowman and to the snowman's eyes that could see into the other window. He felt again the presence of such a comic, powerful figure—felt that, as with the penetrating sightlessness of a blind man, whose eyes look inwards and think, that these slate-black eyes of the snowman knew all about him, about the house, about the morning. . . .

In momentary puzzlement he saw down by his shoes and through the fluttering screen of his eyelids an old newspaper folded out thin and flat on the floor. An old paper, dead a fortnight at least. Muzzed photographs proclaimed faces among the headlines. Headlines of violence—deaths, robberies, accidents, manslaughters, murders. All these had happened two weeks ago, all were forgotten: now this very fact seemed to prove their greater reality. This in turn suggested instantly that such things being true, they could happen again, in the future, or now, and anywhere, and at any time. They were no longer the fabrications of the days, the served up cereal of breakfast news— but histories, true stories happening in certain houses visible in ordinary streets on the turning of a corner: associated much with the daylight, and with suburbs, though no longer with the laurel groves and decrepitudes of old empty houses but now with linoleum and the vacuum cleaner, rolls of wallpaper and clear windows and all the loneliness of one clean house in an endless row of villas. Neal was suddenly seized between his legs with a terror, staring at the white wall of plaster facing his nose he was wildly seized with the idea of *possibility*, of what might happen at any time to anyone and what suddenly he was sure might be happening to him and his morning and his house then at that moment. What risks, what terrible risks are taken at each moment of existence! How one moves so assured that such an accident or such an attack would never be ours, so bolstered against events by the report of similar happenings arranged neatly round the inviolate circle of our own acquaintance, so confident in our will to live of our capacity for living unharmed. And yet . . . all our lives, what might have happened! What *did* happen, two miles away, round the corner, or at this place we chose not to visit on the whim of a moment in favour of that other place to which we went. And when an accident does occur, when something really at last happens to us—then how personal it feels, personally divided from all other experience, never part of the chain of all accidents but something entirely individual and private. . . . Yet each illusionary event in each reported suburb is in no way less ours. The turnings, in retrospect, that might have been taken! The walks up this street, or down that alley, the pauses for the indecision of this way or that, pauses to light a cigarette in the shelter of some strange doorway— when behind us the door might quietly have opened, and in the darkness within what figure might have stood, with what lunatic intention?

But here—Neal shouted within his mind—there is no door! Only wall, muffling barricade of soundless wall. So huge in that second the little wall stretched its plaster endlessly to either side of the silence—no fissure, no picture hung like a window to the imagination, no nail-mark, only plaster, plaster, plaster white as a paper blind, negative, dry as the stone-mason's yard, as the doll-shop, the sculptor's floor, the powdered province of the concrete-mixer, a white and powdery blankness blinding everything inevitably with only the answer NO. And if this is happening, Neal's mind screamed, if this moment is the *now*, then this is the unique fraction of time given me ever to act, and if I don't act what might not be stopped, or what might I even now be too late to stop . . .? He threw down the paint-pot, its paint spewed and piled avidly out onto the boards, he was at the door tugging round the handle, clattering out, tugging at the second door-handle in the hall, and then had flung open the second door and was on the threshold of that other room beyond the wall.

What faced him then was a waxwork scene.

Still, suspended, in that clean daylit second as washed as the sober morning ever was—there the familiar room stood photographed. In it, two figures. Elsa his wife bent over the desk, motionless. Neal saw the hump of her bent back, the blue house-coat humped with the lines of her body, her hand outstretched and reaching, her face bent awkwardly round towards the door. The other, the sweep, crouching by the fireplace, one of the thick sooted rods held in his hand. Over the fireplace hung the black sweep-screen, and against this in that second Neal saw the sweep's brown-overalled legs braced astride, the body low, agile and frogged with a leaping force, the blunt rod swung back in the hand beneath his face bent forward in profile towards Elsa's body.

Then, like a halted film put suddenly into motion, the sweep's rod curled round towards the fireplace, and with it these braced legs bent down to their knees on the hearth: and Elsa's face, flickering for a moment with indecision, blank as a face awakening from the possibility of having dreamt, suddenly realised Neal's presence and smiled with what seemed to be relief; the lips said: ' Oh, it's you! ' And the out-stretched hand drew forth the book for which behind the desk it had been reaching—and she stood up.

The sweep was rattling his sticks far up the chimney, absorbed in the mouse-like sound of a little mortar pattering down behind the sheet.

Neal stood foolishly, his one hand still on the door-handle, his other collapsed slackly to his side. Outside, the sun glinted on a million sparkling thawdrops, the tinselled light threw about the room a festive clarity as in a bright nordic room. Nothing, Neal said to himself, nothing. . . .

Then, as often, things inanimate took charge. There came a sigh and a light thud from the garden. Neal turned quickly to the window. The snowman's head had toppled off its thawed neck, and now lay, face upwards, staring blankly into the blind sky.

The Judge's House

BY BRAM STOKER

The author of Dracula *rarely quite pulled it off again. His other stories usually overstep the mark with resulting giggles rather than shudders. But this, easily the best of his short tales, is an entertaining gusty ghost story for reading—aloud or otherwise—in the half light. Critics may complain that it has weaknesses—and it has, both literary and technical—and that the theme is appropriated from Le Fanu (so was* Dracula's*). Nevertheless this boasts a* dénouement *which is non-existent in the Irish master's original and it is worth its place for one insidious line alone : ' Rats is bogeys and bogeys is rats!'*

WHEN THE TIME for his examination drew near, Malcolm Malcolmson made up his mind to go somewhere to read by himself. He feared the attractions of the seaside, and also he feared completely rural isolation, for of old he knew its charms, and so he determined to find some unpretentious little town where there would be nothing to distract him. He refrained from asking suggestions from any of his friends, for he argued that each would recommend some place of which he had knowledge, and where he had already acquaintances. As Malcolmson wished to avoid friends he had no wish to encumber himself with the attention of friends' friends, and so he determined to look out for a place for himself. He packed a portmanteau with some clothes and all the books he required, and then took a ticket for the first name on the local time-table which he did not know.

When at the end of three hours' journey he alighted at Benchurch, he felt satisfied that he had so far obliterated his tracks as to be sure of having a peaceful opportunity of pursuing his studies. He went straight to the one inn which the sleepy little place contained, and put up for the night. Benchurch was a market town, and once in three weeks was crowded to excess, but for the remainder of the twenty-one days it was as attractive as a desert. Malcolmson looked around the day after his arrival to try to find quarters more isolated than even so quiet an inn as The Good Traveller afforded. There was only one place which took his fancy, and it certainly satisfied his wildest ideas regarding quiet; in fact, quiet was not the proper word to apply to it—desolation was the only term conveying any suitable idea of its isolation. It was an old, rambling, heavy-built house of the Jacobean style, with heavy gables and windows, unusually small, and set higher than was customary in such houses, and was surrounded with a high brick wall massively built. Indeed, on examination, it looked more like a fortified house than an ordinary dwelling. But all these things pleased Malcolmson. 'Here,' he thought, 'is the very spot I have been looking for.' His joy was increased when he realised that it was not at present inhabited.

From the post-office he got the name of the agent, who was rarely surprised at the application to rent a part of the old house. Mr. Carnford, the local lawyer and agent, was a genial old gentleman and frankly confessed his delight at anyone being willing to live in the house.

'To tell you the truth,' said he, 'I should be only too happy, on behalf of the owners, to let anyone have the house rent free for a term of years if only to accustom the people here to see it inhabited. It has been so long empty that some kind of absurd prejudice has grown up about it, and this can be best put down by its occupation—if only,' he added with a sly glance at Malcolmson, 'by a scholar like yourself, who wants its quiet for a time.'

Malcolmson thought it needless to ask the agent about the 'absurd prejudice'; he knew he would get more information, if he should require it, on that subject from other quarters. He paid his three months' rent, got a receipt, and the name of an old woman who would probably undertake to 'do' for him, and came away with the keys in his pocket. He then went to the landlady of the inn, who was a cheerful and most kindly person, and asked her advice as to such stores and provisions as he would be likely to require. She threw up her hands in amazement when he told her where he was going to settle himself.

'Not in the Judge's House!' she said, and grew pale as she spoke. He explained the locality of the house, saying that he did not know its name. When he had finished she answered:

'Aye, sure enough—sure enough the very place! It is the Judge's House sure enough.' He asked her to tell him about the place, why so called, and what there was against it. She told him that it was so called locally because it had been many years before—how long she could not say, as she was herself from another part of the country, but she thought it must have been a hundred years or more—the abode of a judge who was held in great terror on account of his harsh sentences and his hostility to prisoners at Assizes. As to what there was against the house itself she could not tell. She had often asked, but no one could inform her; but there was a general feeling that there was *something*, and for her own part she would not take all the money in Drinkwater's Bank and stay in the house an hour by herself. Then she apologised to Malcolmson for her disturbing talk.

'It is too bad of me, sir, and you—and a young gentleman, too, if you will pardon me saying it—going to live there all alone. If you were my boy—and you'll excuse me for saying it—you wouldn't sleep there a night, not if I had to go there myself and pull the big alarm bell that's on the roof.' The good creature was so manifestly in earnest, and was so kindly, that Malcolmson, although amused, was touched. He told her how much he appreciated her interest in him, and added:

'But, my dear Mrs. Witham, indeed you need not be concerned about me! A man who is reading for the Mathematical Tripos has too much to think of to be disturbed by any of these mysterious "somethings", and his work is of too exact and prosaic a kind to allow of his having any corner in his mind for mysteries of any kind. Harmonical Progression, Permutations and Combinations, and Elliptic Functions have sufficient mysteries for me!' Mrs. Witham kindly undertook to see after his commissions, and he went himself to look for the old woman who had been recommended to him. When he returned to the Judge's House with her, after an interval of a couple of hours, he found Mrs. Witham herself waiting with several men and boys carrying parcels, and an upholsterer's man with a bed in a cart, for she said, though tables and chairs might be all very well, a bed that hadn't been aired for mayhap fifty years was not proper for young bones to lie on. She was evidently curious to see the inside of the house; and though manifestly so afraid of the ' somethings ' that at the slightest sound she clutched on to Malcolmson, whom she never left for a moment, went over the whole place.

After his examination of the house, Malcolmson decided to take up his abode in the great dining-room, which was big enough to serve for all his requirements; and Mrs. Witham, with the aid of the charwoman, Mrs. Dempster, proceeded to arrange matters. When the hampers were brought in and unpacked, Malcolmson saw that with much kind forethought she had sent from her own kitchen sufficient provisions to last for a few days. Before going she expressed all sorts of kind wishes; and at the door turned and said:

' And perhaps, sir, as the room is big and draughty it might be well to have one of those big screens put round your bed at night—though, truth to tell, I would die myself if I were to be so shut in with all kinds of—of " things", that put their heads round the sides, or over the top, and look on me! ' The image which she had called up was too much for her nerves, and she fled incontinently.

Mrs. Dempster sniffed in a superior manner as the landlady disappeared, and remarked that for her own part she wasn't afraid of all the bogeys in the kingdom.

' I'll tell you what it is, sir,' she said; ' bogeys is all kinds and sorts of things—except bogeys! Rats and mice, and beetles; and creaky doors, and loose slates, and broken panes, and stiff drawer handles, that stay out when you pull them and then fall down in the middle of the night. Look at the wainscot of the room! It is old—hundreds of years old! Do you think there's no rats and beetles there? And do you imagine, sir, that you won't see none of them! Rats is bogeys, I tell you, and bogeys is rats; and don't you get to think anything else! '

' Mrs. Dempster,' said Malcolmson gravely, making her a polite bow, ' you know more than a Senior Wrangler! And let me say, that, as a mark of esteem for your indubitable soundness of head and heart, I shall, when I go, give you possession of this house, and let you stay here by yourself for the last two months of my tenancy, for four weeks will serve my purpose.'

' Thank you kindly, sir! ' she answered, ' but I couldn't sleep away from home a night. I am in Greenhow's Charity, and if I slept a night away from my rooms I should lose all I have got to live on. The rules is very strict; and there's too many watching for a vacancy for me to run any risks in the matter. Only for that, sir, I'd gladly come here and attend on you altogether during your stay.'

'My good woman,' said Malcolm hastily, 'I have come here on purpose to obtain solitude; and believe me that I am grateful to the late Greenhow for having so organised his admirable charity—whatever it is—that I am perforce denied the opportunity of suffering from such a form of temptation! Saint Anthony himself could not be more rigid on the point!'

The old woman laughed harshly. 'Ah, you young gentlemen,' she said, 'you don't fear for naught; and belike you'll get all the solitude you want here.' She set to work with her cleaning; and by nightfall, when Malcolmson returned from his walk—he always had one of his books to study as he walked—he found the room swept and tidied, a fire burning in the old hearth, the lamp lit, and the table spread for supper with Mrs. Witham's excellent fare. 'This is comfort, indeed,' he said, as he rubbed his hands.

When he had finished his supper, and lifted the tray to the other end of the great oak dining-table, he got out his books again, put fresh wood on the fire, trimmed his lamp, and set himself down to a spell of real hard work. He went on without pause till about eleven o'clock, when he knocked off for a bit to fix his fire and lamp, and to make himself a cup of tea. He had always been a tea-drinker, and during his college life had sat late at work and had taken tea late. The rest was a great luxury to him, and he enjoyed it with a sense of delicious, voluptuous ease. The renewed fire leaped and sparkled, and threw quaint shadows through the great old room; and as he sipped his hot tea he revelled in the sense of isolation from his kind. Then it was that he began to notice for the first time what a noise the rats were making.

'Surely,' he thought, 'they cannot have been at it all the time I was reading. Had they been, I must have noticed it!' Presently, when the noise increased, he satisfied himself that it was really new. It was evident that at first the rats had been frightened at the presence of a stranger, and the fire and lamp; but that as the time went on they had grown bolder and were now disporting themselves as was their wont.

How busy they were! and hark to the strange noises! Up and down behind the old wainscot, over the ceiling and under the floor they raced, and gnawed, and scratched! Malcolmson smiled to himself as he recalled to mind the saying of Mrs. Dempster, 'Bogeys is rats, and rats is bogeys!' The tea began to have its effect of intellectual and nervous stimulus, he saw with joy another long spell of work to be done before the night was past, and in the sense of security which it gave him, he allowed himself the luxury of a good look round the room. He took his lamp in one hand, and went all around, wondering that so quaint and beautiful an old house had been so long neglected. The carving of the oak on the panels of the wainscot was fine, and on and round the doors and windows it was beautiful and of rare merit. There were some old pictures on the walls, but they were coated so thick with dust and dirt that he could not distinguish any detail of them, though he held his lamp as high as he could over his head. Here and there as he went round he saw some crack or hole blocked for a moment by the face of a rat with its bright eyes glittering in the light, but in an instant it was gone, and a squeak and a scamper followed.

The thing that most struck him, however, was the rope of the great alarm bell on the roof, which hung down in a corner of the room on the right-hand side of the fireplace. He pulled up close to the hearth a great high-backed carved oak chair, and sat down to his last cup of tea. When this was done he made up the fire, and went back to his work, sitting at the corner of the table, having the fire to his left. For a while the rats disturbed him somewhat with their perpetual scampering, but he got accustomed to the noise as one does to the ticking of a clock or to the roar of moving water; and he became so immersed in his work that everything in the world, except the problem which he was trying to solve, passed away from him.

He suddenly looked up, his problem was still unsolved, and there was in the air that sense of the hour before the dawn, which is so dread to doubtful life. The noise of the rats had ceased. Indeed it seemed to him that it must have ceased but lately and that it was the sudden cessation which had disturbed him. The fire had fallen low, but still it threw out a deep red glow. He started in spite of his *sang froid*.

There on the great high-backed carved oak chair by the right side of the fireplace sat an enormous rat, steadily glaring at him with baleful eyes. He made a motion to it as though to hunt it away, but it did not stir. Then he made the motion of throwing something. Still it did not stir, but showed its great white teeth angrily, and its cruel eyes shone in the lamplight with an added vindictiveness.

Malcolmson felt amazed, and seizing the poker from the hearth ran at it to kill it. Before, however, he could strike it, the rat, with a squeak that sounded like the concentration of hate, jumped upon the floor, and, running up the rope of the alarm bell, disappeared in the darkness beyond the range of the green-shaded lamp. Instantly, the noisy scampering of the rats in the wainscot began again. By this time Malcolmson's mind was quite off the problem; and as a shrill cock-crow outside told him of the approach of morning, he went to bed.

He slept so soundly that he was not even waked by Mrs. Dempster coming in to make up his room. It was only when she had tidied up the place and got his breakfast ready and tapped on the screen which closed in his bed that he woke. He was a little tired still after his night's hard work, but a strong cup of tea soon freshened him up, and, taking his book, he went out for his morning walk, bringing with him a few sandwiches lest he should not care to return till dinner-time. He found a quiet walk between high elms some way outside the town, and here he spent the greater part of the day studying his Laplace. On his return he looked in to see Mrs. Witham and to thank her for her kindness. When she saw him coming through the diamond-paned bay-window of her sanctum she came out to meet him and asked him in. She looked at him searchingly and shook her head as she said:

'You must not overdo it, sir. You are paler this morning than you should be. Too late hours and too hard work on the brain isn't good for any man! But tell me, sir, how did you pass the night? Well, I hope? But, my heart! sir, I was glad when Mrs. Dempster told me this morning that you were all right and sleeping sound when she went in.'

'Oh, I was all right,' he answered, smiling, 'the "somethings" didn't worry me, as yet. Only the rats; and they had a circus, I tell you, all over the place. There was one wicked looking old devil that sat up on my own chair by the fire, and wouldn't go till I took the poker to him, and then he ran up the rope of the alarm bell and got to some-where up the wall or the ceiling—I couldn't see where, it was so dark.'

'Mercy on us,' said Mrs. Witham, 'an old devil, and sitting on a chair by the fireside! Take care, sir! take care! There's many a true word spoken in jest.'

'How do you mean? 'Pon my word I don't understand.'

'An old devil! The old devil, perhaps. There! sir, you needn't laugh,' for Malcolmson had broken into a hearty peal. 'You young folks thinks it easy to laugh at things that makes older ones shudder. Never mind, sir! never mind! Please God, you'll laugh all the time. It's what I wish you myself!' and the good lady beamed all over in sympathy with his enjoyment, her fears gone for a moment.

'Oh, forgive me!' said Malcolmson presently. 'Don't think me rude; but the idea was too much for me—that the old devil himself was on the chair last night!' And at the thought he laughed again. Then he went home to dinner.

This evening the scampering of the rats began earlier; indeed it had been going on before his arrival, and only ceased whilst his presence by its freshness disturbed them. After dinner he sat by the fire for a while and had a smoke; and then, having cleared his table, began to work as before. Tonight the rats disturbed him more than they had done on the previous night. How they scampered up and down and under and over! How they squeaked and scratched and gnawed! How they, getting bolder by degrees, came to the mouths of their holes and to the chinks and cracks and crannies in the wainscoting till their eyes shone like tiny lamps as the firelight rose and fell. But to him, now doubtless accustomed to them, their eyes were not wicked; only their playfulness touched him. Sometimes the boldest of them made sallies out on the floor or along the mouldings of the wainscot. Now and again as they disturbed him Malcolmson made a sound to frighten them, smiting the table with his hand or giving a fierce 'Hsh, Hsh,' so that they fled straightway to their holes.

And so the early part of the night wore on; and despite the noise, Malcolmson got more and more immersed in his work.

All at once he stopped, as on the previous night, being overcome by a sudden sense of silence. There was not the faintest sound of gnaw, or scratch, or squeak. The silence was as of the grave. He remembered the odd occurrence of the previous night, and instinctively he looked at the chair standing close by the fireside. And then a very odd sensation thrilled through him.

There, on the high-backed carved oak chair beside the fireplace sat the same enormous rat, steadily glaring at him with baleful eyes.

Instinctively he took the nearest thing to his hand, a book of logarithms, and flung it at it. The book was badly aimed and the rat did not stir, so again the poker performance of the previous night was repeated; and again the rat, being closely pursued, fled up the rope of the alarm bell. Strangely too, the departure of this rat was instantly followed by the renewal of the noise made by the general rat community. On this occasion, as on the previous one, Malcolmson could not see at what part of the room the rat disappeared, for the green shade of his lamp left the upper part of the room in darkness, and the fire had burned low.

On looking at his watch he found it was close on midnight; and, not sorry for the *divertissement*, he made up his fire and made himself his nightly pot of tea. He had got through a good spell of work, and thought himself entitled to a cigarette; and so he sat on the great carved oak chair before the fire and enjoyed it. Whilst smoking he began to think that he would like to know where the rat disappeared to, for he had certain ideas for the morrow not entirely disconnected with a rat-trap. Accordingly he lit another lamp and placed it so that it would shine well into the right-hand corner of the wall by the fireplace. Then he got all the books he had with him, and placed them handy to throw at the vermin. Finally he lifted the rope of the alarm bell and placed the end of it on the table, fixing the extreme end under the lamp. As he handled it he could not help noticing how pliable it was, especially for so strong a rope, and one not in use. 'You could hang a man with it,' he thought to himself. When his preparations were made he looked around, and said complacently:

'There now, my friend, I think we shall learn something of you this time!' He began his work again, and though as before somewhat disturbed at first by the noise of the rats, soon lost himself in his propositions and problems.

Again he was called to his immediate surroundings suddenly. This time it might not have been the sudden silence only which took his attention; there was a slight movement of the rope, and the lamp moved. Without stirring, he looked to see if his pile of books was within range, and then cast his eye along the rope. As he looked he saw the great rat drop from the rope on to the oak armchair and sit there glaring at him. He raised a book in his right hand and, taking careful aim, flung it at the rat. The latter, with a quick movement, sprang aside and dodged the missile. He then took another book, and a third, and flung them one after another at the rat, but each time unsuccessfully. At last, as he stood with a book poised in his hand to throw, the rat squeaked and seemed afraid. This made Malcolmson more than ever eager to strike, and the book flew and struck the rat a resounding blow. It gave a terrified squeak, and turning on its pursuer a look of terrible malevolence, ran up the chair-back and made a great jump to the rope of the alarm bell and ran up it like lightning. The lamp rocked under the sudden strain, but it was a heavy one and did not topple over. Malcolmson kept his eyes on the rat and saw it, by the light of the second lamp, leap to a moulding of the wainscot and disappear through a hole in one of the great pictures which hung on the wall, obscured and invisible through its coating of dirt and dust.

'I shall look up my friend's habitation in the morning,' said the student, as he went over to collect his books. 'The third picture from the fireplace; I shall not forget.' He picked up the books one by one, commenting on them as he lifted them. '*Conic Sections* he does not mind, nor *Cycloidal Oscillations*, nor the *Principia*, nor *Quaternions*, nor *Thermodynamics*. Now for the book that fetched him!' Malcolmson took it up and looked at it. As he did so he started; he glanced round uneasily and shivered slightly, as he murmured to himself:

'The Bible my mother gave me! What an odd coincidence.' He sat down to work again, and the rats in the wainscot renewed their gambols. They did not disturb him, however; somehow their presence gave him a sense of companionship. But he could not attend to his work, and after striving to master the subject on which he was engaged gave it up in despair, and went to bed as the first streak of dawn stole in through the eastern window.

He slept heavily but uneasily, and dreamed much; and when Mrs. Dempster woke him late in the morning he seemed ill at ease, and for a few minutes did not seem to realise exactly where he was. His first request rather surprised the servant.

'Mrs. Dempster, when I am out today I wish you would get the steps and dust or wash these pictures—specially that one the third from the fireplace—I want to see what they are.'

Late in the afternoon Malcolmson worked at his books in the shaded walk, and the cheerfulness of the previous day came back to him as the day wore on, and he found that his reading was progressing well. He had worked out to a satisfactory conclusion all the problems which had as yet baffled him, and it was in a state of jubilation that he paid a visit to Mrs. Witham at The Good Traveller. He found a stranger in the cosy sitting-room with the landlady, who was introduced to him as Dr. Thornhill. She was not quite at ease, and this, combined with the Doctor's plunging at once into a series of questions, made Malcolmson come to the conclusion that his presence was not an accident, so without preliminary he said:

'Dr. Thornhill, I shall with pleasure answer any question you may choose to ask me if you will answer me one question first.'

The Doctor seemed surprised, but he smiled and answered at once. 'Done! What is it?'

'Did Mrs. Witham ask you to come here and advise me?'

Dr. Thornhill for a moment was taken aback, and Mrs. Witham got fiery red and turned away; but the doctor was a frank and ready man and he answered at once and openly:

'She did: but she didn't intend you to know it. I suppose it was my clumsy haste that made you suspect. She told me that she did not like the idea of your being in that house all by yourself, and that she thought that you took too much strong tea. In fact, she wants me to advise you if possible to give up the tea and the very late hours. I was a keen student in my time, so I suppose I may take the liberty of a college man, and without offence, advise you not quite as a stranger.'

Malcolmson with a bright smile held out his hand. 'Shake! as they say in America,' he said. 'I must thank you for your kindness and Mrs. Witham too, and your kindness deserves a return on my part. I promise to take no more strong tea—no tea at all till you let me—and I shall go to bed tonight at one o'clock at latest. Will that do?'

'Capital,' said the Doctor. 'Now tell us all that you noticed in the old house.' And so Malcolmson then and there told in minute detail all that had happened in the last two nights. He was interrupted every now and then by some exclamation from Mrs. Witham, till finally when he told of the episode of the Bible the landlady's pent-up emotions found vent in a shriek; and it was not till a stiff glass of brandy and water had been administered that she grew composed again. Dr. Thornhill listened with a face of growing gravity, and when the narrative was complete and Mrs. Witham had been restored he asked:

'The rat always went up the rope of the alarm bell?'

'Always.'

'I suppose you know,' said the Doctor, 'what the rope is?'

'No!'

It is,' said the Doctor slowly, ' the very rope which the hangman used for all the victims of the Judge's judicial rancour!' Here he was interrupted by another scream from Mrs. Witham, and steps had to be taken for her recovery. Malcolmson having found that it was close to his dinner-hour, had gone home before her complete recovery.

When Mrs. Witham was herself again she almost assailed the Doctor with angry questions as to what he meant by putting such horrible ideas into the poor young man's mind. ' He has quite enough there already to upset him,' she added. Dr. Thornhill replied:

' My dear madam, I had a distinct purpose in it! I wanted to draw his attention to the bell rope, and to fix it there. It may be that he is in a highly overwrought state, and has been studying too much, although I am bound to say that he seems as sound and healthy a young man, mentally and bodily, as ever I saw—but then the rats—and that suggestion of the devil.' The doctor shook his head and went on. ' I would have offered to go and stay the first night with him but that I felt sure it would have been a cause of offence. He may get in the night some strange fright or hallucination; and if he does I want him to pull that rope. All alone as he is it will give us warning, and we may reach him in time to be of service. I shall be sitting up pretty late tonight and shall keep my ears open. Do not be alarmed if Benchurch gets a surprise before morning.'

' Oh, Doctor, what do you mean? What do you mean?'

' I mean this: that possibly—nay, more probably—we shall hear the great alarm bell from the Judge's House tonight,' and the Doctor made about as effective an exit as could be thought of.

When Malcolmson arrived home he found that it was a little after his usual time, and Mrs. Dempster had gone away—the rules of Green-how's Charity were not to be neglected. He was glad to see that the place was bright and tidy with a cheerful fire and a well-trimmed lamp. The evening was colder than might have been expected in April, and a heavy wind was blowing with such rapidly-increasing strength that there was every promise of a storm during the night. For a few minutes after his entrance the noise of the rats ceased; but so soon as they became accustomed to his presence they began again. He was glad to hear them, for he felt once more the feeling of companionship in their noise, and his mind ran back to the strange fact that they only ceased to manifest themselves when that other—the great rat with the baleful eyes—came upon the scene. The reading-lamp only was lit and its green shade kept the ceiling and the upper part of the room in darkness, so that the cheerful light from the hearth spreading over the floor and shining on the white cloth laid over the end of the table was warm and cheery. Malcolmson sat down to his dinner with a good appetite and a buoyant spirit. After his dinner and a cigarette he sat steadily down to work, determined not to let anything disturb him, for he remembered his promise to the doctor, and made up his mind to make the best of the time at his disposal.

For an hour or so he worked all right, and then his thoughts began to wander from his books. The actual circumstances around him, the calls on his physical attention, and his nervous susceptibility were not to be denied. By this time the wind had become a gale, and the gale a storm. The old house, solid though it was, seemed to shake to its foundations, and the storm roared and raged through its many chimneys and its queer old gables, producing strange, unearthly sounds in the empty rooms and corridors. Even the great alarm bell on the roof must have felt the force of the wind, for the rope rose and fell slightly, as though the bell were moved a little from time to time, and the limber rope fell on the oak floor with a hard and hollow sound.

As Malcolmson listened to it he bethought himself of the doctor's words, ' It is the rope which the hangman used for the victims of the Judge's judicial rancour,' and he went over to the corner of the fireplace and took it in his hand to look at it. There seemed a sort of deadly interest in it, and as he stood there he lost himself for a moment in speculation as to who these victims were, and the grim wish of the Judge to have such a ghastly relic ever under his eyes. As he stood there the swaying of the bell on the roof still lifted the rope now and again; but presently there came a new sensation—a sort of tremor in the rope, as though something was moving along it.

Looking up instinctively, Malcolmson saw the great rat coming slowly down towards him, glaring at him steadily. He dropped the rope and started back with a muttered curse, and the rat turning ran up the rope and disappeared; at the same instant Malcolmson became conscious that the noise of the rats, which had ceased for a while, began again.

All this set him thinking, and it occurred to him that he had not investigated the lair of the rat or looked at the pictures, as he had intended. He lit the lamp without the shade, and holding it up, went and stood opposite the third picture from the fireplace on the right-hand side where he had seen the rat disappear on the previous night.

At the first glance he started back so suddenly that he almost dropped the lamp. His knees shook, and heavy drops of sweat came on his forehead, and he trembled like an aspen. But he pulled himself together, and after a few seconds stepped forward again, raised the lamp, and examined the picture which had been dusted and washed, and now stood out clearly.

It was of a judge dressed in his robes of scarlet and ermine. His face was strong and merciless, evil, crafty, and vindictive, with a sensual mouth, hooked nose of ruddy colour, and shaped like the beak of a bird of prey. The rest of the face was of a cadaverous colour. The eyes were of peculiar brilliance and with a terribly malignant expression. As he looked at them, Malcolmson grew cold, for he saw there the very counterpart of the eyes of the great rat. The lamp almost fell from his hand: he saw the rat with its baleful eyes peering out through the hole in the corner of the picture, and noted the sudden cessation of the noise of the other rats. However, he pulled himself together, and went on with his examination of the picture.

The Judge was seated in a great high-backed carved oak chair, on the right-hand side of a great stone fireplace, where in the corner, a rope hung down from the ceiling, its end lying coiled on the floor. With a feeling of something like horror, Malcolmson recognised the scene of the room as it stood, and gazed around him in an awe-struck manner as though he expected to find some strange presence behind him. Then he looked over to the corner of the fireplace—and with a loud cry he let the lamp fall from his hand.

There, in the Judge's armchair, with the rope hanging behind, sat the rat with the Judge's baleful eyes, now intensified and with a fiendish leer. Save for the howling of the storm without there was silence.

The fallen lamp recalled Malcolmson to himself. Fortunately it was of metal, and so the oil was not spilt. However, the practical need of attending to it settled at once his nervous apprehensions. When he had turned it out, he wiped his brow and thought for a moment.

' This will not do,' he said to himself. ' If I go on like this I shall become a crazy fool. This must stop! I promised the Doctor I would not take tea. Faith, he was pretty right! My nerves must have been getting into a queer state. Funny I did not notice it. I never felt better in my life. However, I shall not be such a fool again.'

Then he mixed himself a good stiff glass of brandy and water and resolutely sat down to his work.

It was nearly an hour before he looked up from his book, disturbed by the sudden stillness. Without, the wind howled and roared louder than ever, and the rain drove in sheets against the windows, beating like hail on the glass; but within there was no sound whatever save the echo of the wind as it roared in the great chimney, and now and then a hiss as a few raindrops found their way down the chimney in a lull of the storm. The fire had fallen low and had ceased to flame, though it threw out a red glow. Malcolmson listened attentively, and presently heard a thin, squeaking noise, very faint. It came from the corner of the room where the rope hung down, and he thought it was the creaking of the rope on the floor as the swaying of the bell raised and lowered it. Looking up, however, he saw in the dim light the great rat clinging to the rope and gnawing it. The rope was already nearly gnawed through —he could see the lighter colour where the strands were laid bare. As he looked the job was completed, and the severed end of the rope fell clattering on the oaken floor, whilst for an instant the great rat remained like a knob or tassel at the end of the rope, which now began to sway to and fro. Malcolmson felt for a moment another pang of terror as he thought that now the possibility of calling the outer world to his assistance was cut off, but an intense anger took its place, and seizing the book he was reading he hurled it at the rat. The blow was well aimed, but before the missile could reach it the rat dropped off and struck the floor with a soft thud. Malcolmson instantly rushed over towards it, but it darted away and disappeared in the darkness of the shadows of the room. Malcolmson felt that his work was over for the night, and determined then and there to vary the monotony of the proceedings by a hunt for the rat, and took off the green shade of the lamp so as to insure a wider spreading light. As he did so the gloom of the upper part of the room was relieved, and in the new flood of light, great by comparison with the previous darkness, the pictures on the wall stood out boldly. From where he stood, Malcolmson saw right opposite to him the third picture on the wall from the right of the fireplace. And then a great fear began to come upon him.

In the centre of the picture was a great irregular patch of brown canvas, as fresh as when it was stretched on the frame. The background was as before, with chair and chimney-corner and rope, but the figure of the Judge had disappeared.

Malcolmson, almost in a chill of horror, turned slowly round, and then he began to shake and tremble like a man in a palsy. His strength seemed to have left him, and he was incapable of action or movement, hardly even of thought. He could only see and hear.

There, on the great high-backed carved oak chair sat the Judge in his robes of scarlet and ermine, with his baleful eyes glaring vindictively, and a smile of triumph on the resolute, cruel mouth, as he lifted with his hands a *black cap*. Malcolmson felt as if the blood was running from his heart, as one does in moments of prolonged suspense. There was a singing in his ears. Without, he could hear the roar and howl of the tempest, and through it, swept on the storm, came the striking of midnight by the great chimes in the market place. He stood for a space of time that seemed to him endless, still as a statue and with wide-open, horror-struck eyes, breathless. As the clock struck, so the smile of triumph on the Judge's face intensified, and at the last stroke of midnight he placed the black cap on his head.

Slowly and deliberately the Judge rose from his chair and picked up the piece of the rope of the alarm bell which lay on the floor, drew it through his hands as if he enjoyed its touch, and then deliberately began to knot one end of it, fashioning it into a noose. This he tightened and tested with his foot, pulling hard at it till he was satisfied and then making a running noose of it, which he held in his hand. Then he began to move along the table on the opposite side to Malcolmson, keeping his eyes on him until he had passed him, when with a quick movement he stood in front of the door. Malcolmson then began to feel that he was trapped, and tried to think of what he could do. There was some fascination in the Judge's eyes, which he never took off him, and he had, perforce, to look. He saw the Judge approach—still keeping between him and the door—and raise the noose and throw it towards him as if to entangle him. With a great effort he made a quick movement to one side, and saw the rope fall beside him, and heard it strike the oaken floor. Again the Judge raised the noose and tried to ensnare him, ever keeping his baleful eyes fixed on him, and each time by a mighty effort the student just managed to evade it. So this went on for many times, the Judge seeming never discouraged nor discomposed at failure, but playing as a cat does with a mouse. At last in despair, which had reached its climax, Malcolmson cast a quick glance round him. The lamp seemed to have blazed up, and there was a fairly good light in the room. At the many rat-holes and in the chinks and crannies of the wainscot he saw the rats' eyes; and this aspect, that was purely physical, gave him a gleam of comfort. He looked around and saw that the rope of the great alarm bell was laden with rats. Every inch of it was covered with them, and more and more were pouring through the small circular hole in the ceiling whence it emerged, so that with their weight the bell was beginning to sway.

Hark! it had swayed till the clapper had touched the bell. The sound was but a tiny one, but the bell was only beginning to sway, and it would increase.

At the sound the Judge, who had been keeping his eyes fixed on Malcolmson, looked up, and a scowl of diabolical anger overspread his face. His eyes fairly glowed like hot coals, and he stamped his foot with a sound that seemed to make the house shake. A dreadful peal of thunder broke overhead as he raised the rope again, whilst the rats kept running up and down the rope as though working against time. This time, instead of throwing it, he drew close to his victim, and held open the noose as he approached. As he came closer there seemed something paralysing in his very presence, and Malcolmson stood rigid as a corpse. He felt the Judge's icy fingers touch his throat as he adjusted the rope. The noose tightened—tightened. Then the Judge, taking the rigid form of the student in his arms, carried him over and placed him standing in the oak chair, and stepping up beside him, put his hand up and caught the end of the swaying rope of the alarm bell. As he raised his hand the rats fled squeaking, and disappeared through the hole in the ceiling. Taking the end of the noose which was round Malcolmson's neck he tied it to the hanging bell-rope, and then descending, pulled away the chair.

When the alarm bell of the Judge's House began to sound a crowd soon assembled. Lights and torches of various kinds appeared, and soon a silent crowd was hurrying to the spot. They knocked loudly at the door, but there was no reply. Then they burst in the door, and poured into the great dining-room, the doctor at the head.

At the end of the rope of the great bell hung the body of the student, and on the face of the Judge in the picture was a malignant smile.

FUN and GAMES

What's the odds, so long as you're happy
There is no jollity but hath a smack of folly
The heart's mirth doth make the face fair
Pleasant hours fly fast

Game for Anything

BY ROBERT WILLSON

'Now is the time for all good men to come to the aid of the party.'

USED TO THINK that by far the most interesting party games were those which involved a prolonged absence from the room of a man (who would be me) and a woman (who would be a perfectly devastating blonde with laughing blue eyes and a mischievous mouth). I did not like games which called for pencil and paper and a considerable amount of concentration, and I altogether shrank from taking part in any form of charade.

Autres temps autres mœurs. Which strikes me as being a nice, delicate, French way of saying that experience can often be very cruel. At all events, I find that I can now easily resist the temptation to take the fascinating Miss Fenderby by the frozen mit and lead her forth into the dimly-lit corridor, there to play a little game which is as old as time. Frankly, I prefer to be supplied with pencil and paper and told (but with what charm and grace!) to draw a lemon. It's so much less exasperating.

I remember a remarkable incident at a Christmas party once when the hostess, clad in what appeared to be a vast number of petticoats, and with a tea cup tied round her ankle, suddenly burst into the room and began to chant: 'What am I? What am I?'

Her husband, curiously enough, made no attempt to restrain her. Indeed, no one appeared to think that the lady was behaving in other than a perfectly rational manner. But a serious young woman who, I fancy, had been discussing Purist-Functionalist Art with her companion, stopped in the middle of a sentence, put down her coffee cup, and exclaimed delightedly, 'Oh, how delicious! I do love silly games, don't you?'

And her friend, without a moment's hesitation, jumped to his feet and almost shouted, ' I know. I've got it. " There's many a slip twixt cup and lip." '

Well, that seems to be one silly game for you to play at Christmas. And as far as I know there is nothing to prevent your putting over a book or play title with equal abandon if you are rather weak on proverbs. In fact, there is really nothing in the rules to prevent your making quite an exhibition of yourself in any way that happens to take your fancy at a Christmas party. You simply cannot go wrong at this time of year.

But the proceedings, I feel, should begin on a slightly more sober note. And a suitably dignified way of starting the ball rolling is to provide each member of the party with a sheet of paper and a pencil, and then distribute small cards each bearing the name of an object which the recipient has to draw.

This action will naturally evoke shrill cries of protest from all those who rather fancy themselves as artists. It is, therefore, up to the organiser to see that these artistic temperaments are duly supplied with practically impossible subjects.

Anybody, for example, who says, ' But I couldn't even draw a pin! ' should be required (but in the strictest confidence) to draw just that.

After a suitable interval the art work is collected and each effort scrutinised, in turn, by everyone present. I say ' scrutinised ' advisedly, because it is often quite a problem to decide which is the right way up for a turnip and, indeed, whether it isn't a sweet potato anyway.

The drawer of the sketch, recognised and correctly named by the greatest number, is, of course, the *victor ludorum*. But the drawing in each case must be accurately described. If, for instance, you have been briefed to draw a straw hat, and somebody is clever enough to see in your creation the suggestion of some form of head covering, you cannot claim half a mark because he or she, after due deliberation, observes that it might be a—well—a kind of hat thing but on second thoughts, etc. It's a *straw* hat or nothing. I'm sorry, but that's the way it is.

A slightly more energetic pencil and paper game involves the picking of two sides, of equal numbers, one of which must withdraw to the dining-room or, at any rate, to a previously prepared position. An umpire (poor fellow), armed with a list of unlikely subjects, is then dispatched to an isolated position equally accessible to the members of the two opposing sides.

'GO EASY, DEAR. THAT'S THE SUNDAY JOINT!'

At the word 'go' a person from each side is summoned by the umpire who gives them the first word on his list. They must then quickly rejoin their respective teams and, without uttering a syllable, and using only paper and pencil, try and communicate to their fellow playmates by means of a straightforward drawing the word they have been given.

As soon as somebody has guessed the word correctly, another member of the syndicate goes off and obtains the next word from the umpire who will, no doubt, soon be wondering why he didn't stay at home and get down to a nice rowdy game of patience.

The side which, probably by underhand methods, is the first to interpret correctly all the words appearing on the list is, needless to say, the winning team. And the quicker this is accomplished the better, I imagine, the umpire will like it.

Another game calculated to break the ice at a large party is the one in which slips of paper, each bearing the name of a famous character (in fact or in fiction, living or dead), are pinned on to the back of each guest. Nobody knows the identity of the illustrious figure which adorns his back, and he must try and discover, by interrogating his opposite number (who of course can see the name although he may be somewhat hazy about his accomplishments) who he or she is, or was. The individual being thus questioned may only reply with a curt 'yes' or 'no'.

Taking the game a stage further—and you can entirely please yourself about this—as soon as anyone guesses correctly, the fact is duly recorded and another name is pinned on to his back. And so on, until somebody can decently be adjudged the winner.

The last time I played this game the name they pinned on my back was F. E. Smith. Having enlisted the support of a young woman who seemed perfectly anxious to co-operate, I was able, after a great deal of questioning, to narrow my choice down to one of two men, both living, and one of them—to such an extent had I been innocently led astray— was none other than a well-known county cricketer. The other, I fancy, was a jockey.

If your guests happen to be moderately intelligent people, here is a game which will probably show just how moderately intelligent they are. Give everyone a sheet of paper—ruled paper if possible because so few intelligent people are able to draw straight lines. In the left hand column may be written any, or all, of the following: actors (or actresses), statesmen (but, please, not politicians), rivers, authors, flowers, artists. This list, incidentally, can be varied or extended to conform with the cultural attainments of the gathering.

Open a book at random and take the first six-letter word on the left-hand page, which we will assume is 'basket'. This word should be written across the top of the page so that each letter has a column of its own underneath.

The players now write down, in the appropriate column, all the well-known actors, statesmen, rivers etc., they can think of whose names begin with the letters b, a, s, k, e, t. The more they get naturally the more intelligent they are. But when any two people produce the same name the one cancels the other out, and it's just too bad. There should, of course, be a time limit for this game, and useful adjuncts are the *Encyclopaedia Britannica* and the *Dictionary of National Biography*.

Perhaps it is time we sent somebody out of the room so that we can make him feel awfully stupid when he comes back by getting him to try

'HOLD IT STEADY, LADS—IT'S A DIFFICULT ANGLE.'

'CLUMSY! RIGHT ON MY CORN AGAIN!'

and find out what we have been discussing during his absence. He can only get us to answer ' yes ' or ' no ' to his questions, and it is surprising how long it will take him to discover that the object we had fixed on was—shall we say?—his left eyebrow.

Here are two games to test (*a*) your powers of observation, and (*b*) your memory.

Place a number of unlikely objects round the room—a safety-pin on the floor, a thimble on the top of a picture-frame, a button on the settee, and so on. Then while everyone is busily engaged in compiling a list of the obviously misplaced articles, you can go and pour yourself out a well-deserved drink.

The other game merely consists of placing on view, for not more than thirty seconds, a tray containing as many wildly assorted articles as space can be found for. The idea is to memorize as many articles as possible within the stipulated time. When the tray has been removed, and everybody is either writing furiously or else feverishly sucking the ends of their pencils, there is absolutely no reason why you shouldn't go and pour yourself out another well-deserved drink.

Covering up, or removing, the manufacturer's name, together with that of the product, from a selection of well-known newspaper or magazine advertisements provides another good memory-cum-observation test. Display a dozen or so of the advertisements, having first carefully obliterated all clues, and see how many products can be correctly named. The result will probably make you wonder just how much it pays to advertise.

Two games which might be described (but not necessarily by this writer) as a ' source of endless laughter and amusement ' are the Nose and Matchbox game and—correct me if I'm wrong—Fishing for the Apple.

For the first, two teams line up in single file, one opposite the other, facing their respective leaders. Two ordinary matchbox cases are produced and the leaders, in their own time, ' peg ' these on to the ends of their noses. The object of the game is now, at a given signal, to transfer the matchbox cases from nose to nose down the line, without using the hands, in the shortest possible time. If the cases drop on the floor —they will—they must go back to the first nose again. From my own limited experience of this game, unless all the noses taking part are of roughly the same size, there is little chance of a definite result.

Fishing for the apple consists of placing a large bowl (or pail) of water in the middle of the room, and bullying or cajoling some unfortunate member of the party to try and fish out, with his mouth, an apple which is floating on the surface. To plunge the head right into the receptacle and force the apple to the bottom, thus enabling one to get one's teeth into it, is not, strictly speaking, legitimate. But— and I have this on the best authority—it's the only way.

Have you ever sat astride an empty quart bottle, with your ankles crossed and supporting yourself with only one hand at a time, and tried to light a candle which is held in one hand with a match from a box held in another? Shall I say all that again?

But really, I think it's about time we got ready to go home. When a party begins to descend to this sort of level I cannot help feeling that we should quietly draw our hostess aside, say how much we have enjoyed ourselves, and retire as gracefully as possible while there is yet time. But after all, it *is* Christmas. . . .

Talking
of Parties

A practical dialogue

BY ROSAMOND HARCOURT-SMITH

*

Caroline :

HENRY has asked twenty-five people to a party here on Boxing-night,
including his mother who was a colonel in the A.T.S. Gertrude insists
on going home to her Mum for Christmas week so that leaves me to
cook the dinner, arrange the house and receive the guests. You must
both help me.

Charles :

I shall come and cook the food.

Caroline :

Oh you love! I hoped you'd say that.

Emmeline :

And I will arrange the flowers and the rooms and you shall just
look beautiful and charm your guests.

Caroline :

Do you really think we've enough space in this tiny flat for twenty-five people?

Charles :

The best party I've been to for years was given last month in my hostess's bedroom and that of her child: the rest of the flat consisted of a kitchen and a bathroom. No one who was not a friend of the family could have recognised the rooms for what they were. They just seemed like two charming salons. Force of character and the grand manner.

Caroline :

Where did the child sleep?

Charles :

In the bath I suspect. I didn't ask.

Emmeline :

If you like Christmas and you like giving parties it's all quite easy. Personally I adore tinsel and presents and doing up parcels and pricking myself with holly and thinking about food.

Caroline :

I think I'd rather go to a party than give one.

Charles :

Well, you practically will be going to this one if Emmeline and I arrange it for you.

Caroline :

Can we have a tree?

Charles :

You *must* have a tree.

Caroline :

Nearly all my pre-war trimmings are broken or tatty.

Emmeline :

I never had any real trimmings since the war; all mine got left in France. But I always had a tree and made the decorations myself. The best I ever did was covered all over with bows of narrow metal ribbon in Glorious Technicolors of pink, blue and acid yellow. The next best had hundreds of silver balls, which were maddening to make, and red candles.

Caroline :

I once had a beau, long before I met Henry, who was as poor as poor, but such fun. He really adored enjoying himself. One Christmas he decided it was his turn to invite the people who'd asked him to grand parties. He spent all the money he could raise on food and drink and found there was nothing left to buy trimmings for the tree, which had been given him as a present by the greengrocer where he'd bought the peaches.

Charles :

Which he soaked in champagne, of course?

Caroline :

Of course, Charles; don't ask silly questions—he *knew* about giving parties. Well, he went back to the greengrocer, explained his pass and bought on tick some of those flat boxes of tangerines which you used to be able to buy for next to nothing. He painted the tree white, like snow, and hung the fruit, some in their silver paper, some naked orange,

from the branches. When the candles were lit it was so strange and lovely that all the rich guests wanted to run home, tear the tinsel balls off their own trees and hang up tangerines. Talking of candles, Caroline, you must get out every candelabrum you possess and have your rooms candle-lit.

Charles :

Oh, I do so agree! Candle-light makes everyone feel romantic or cosy—or both. I never understood why Mother and her friends veiled their candles like so many Victorian widows. The horrid little silk shades painted by whimsical gentlewomen always got burnt; in any case they never gave half so becoming a light as the lovely naked flames. Besides, grease running down the side of a candle like a tiny frozen Niagara can be so lovely but grease running over a metal holder is never attractive. I always feel about grease that——

Emmeline :

Darling, we haven't time to waste on grease. You can have a delicious orgy picking it off the furniture the day after the party. What we must now decide upon is the food, and of course the drink.

Charles :

Only diplomats and film executives can get enough champagne nowadays, so you'll have to eke out whatever gin and whisky you've got with something else. Beer is very lowering on Christmas night, so what about mulled claret? Algerian wine disguises very well if you add sugar, lots of spices and serve it very hot.

Caroline :

If we had dozens of eggs we could make that scrumptious punch you see in American advertisements.

Charles :

Sweet Caroline, do keep your pretty toes on the ground. What would you like to give your guests to eat?

Emmeline :

Don't be such a tease, Charles. We all know what we'd *like* to give our guests to eat. Turkeys stuffed with foie gras, truffles cooked in champagne, enormous great boxes of crystallised fruit, salad made from Avocado pears——

Charles:

Well, you'd better start off with soupe à l'oignon served in the iron pot it's cooked in. Everyone likes it and it doesn't ravish the rations, except of course the cheese. Then your main dish must be cold for, as you'll have no servants it will have to be cooked the day before, otherwise we shall all be deadbeat and scarlet in the face by eight o'clock. I suggest turkeys, or geese, or ducks, with a ham or tongue if you can get them; two cold salads, one potato, and the other Belgian endive with orange. Then a cold pudding. An ice made of the blackcurrants you bottled last summer would be heaven, or zabaglione——

Caroline:

Feet on the ground, sweet Charles! I seem to remember an egg yolk a person?

Charles:

Well, a chocolate mousse. That takes the eggs further as you use the whites as well. Why not a fruit salad?

Caroline:

Oh, *not* a fruit salad?

Charles:

Darling, you're so old-fashioned. It's only the sort with bits of banana and peeled grapes floating in a company of apples and pears that's so depressing. A new one made of bottled strawberries and

fresh oranges, or bottled quince and fresh South African plums would be delicious. By the way, unless you can rely on your mother-in-law, the colonel, playing bat-woman, I advise you to hire a man-servant for the evening. You can't really enjoy yourself if you're harrying round seeing who's been fed and if the dirty glasses have been cleared away. As hostess, you must look as if you'd just floated down off a Tiepolo cloud; I always think it's so rude to look tired at your own party.

Caroline :

As it's Christmas, do you think we ought to play games?

Charles :

It all depends on what games you mean. Most people like poker, rummy, or vingt-et-un. *In the Manner of the Word* can be fun if the party is small and intimate but preserve me from a lot of grown-ups romping at musical chairs or puss-in-the-corner. A collection of adults ought to be happy enough left together in a pretty room with food and drink without being organised.

Emmeline :

How I do agree about romping! I was brought up in a county where *Sardines* was the fashionable game. I always found myself in a dusty cupboard in my best dress having my neck tickled by a fluffy moustache. I think a cupboard's such an uncomfortable place for that sort of thing.

Charles :

I knew a young diplomatic couple who must have been brought up in the same county as you, Emmeline. At their first foreign post they invited all the elegant society who had entertained them, to a Christmas party, lined them up on either side of the dining-room and then invited bejewelled beauties and spoilt ambassadors to blow feathers across the mahogany table. After that they played *Are you there Brother John ?* where the players are blindfold and hit each other with rolled-up newspapers. They had to play this with each other as no one else would join in. Then they had *Oranges and Lemons* and *Hunt the Slipper*. They explained to their guests that this was a typically English evening, and as neither of them possessed the slightest sense of fun we must assume they supposed it was. There is no doubt they were largely responsible for the war, as the German Ambassador certainly wrote home confirming the growing belief that the English were in their dotage.

Caroline :

I always find that the end of the party is the worst part for the hostess. However much she may want to take the nice-looking man brought by someone else round the house she always has to stay stuck in the drawing-room being polite to departing friends.

Emmeline :

Never mind, darling. You get your own back when it's your turn as a guest. And thank-you telephone messages next morning are always a comfort. . . . And now, Caroline, proud mother of three, you must help *me*. Julia's children are coming for the holidays and I have to give a party for under-fives.

Caroline :

Oh, children's parties aren't difficult. They get so excited, poor pets, that provided they are given lots of delicious things to eat they always enjoy themselves.

Emmeline :

When I was a child I hoped against hope that I should be given the fairy-doll off the top of the Christmas tree. I never got it and every party held a crumpled rose-leaf for me.

Caroline :

Poor pet, you shall have the fairy-doll off my tree. Now, about the children. As soon as the last guest has arrived and had its shoes changed, you all go in to tea. You'll put a favour, of course, in front of every plate. Paper hats you can find in every toy shop now, or those little earthenware figures, which I'm afraid were made in Japan, have a terrific success. Tea must be very showy, even to the point of ostentation. Chocolate biscuits all over the place, lots of little pretty cakes (no one at a party can wade through a bun), an iced Christmas cake with snow-men skating on it, heaps of crackers and, naturally, jellies.

Charles :

Do you remember the jellies when we were children? They were orange quarters with real skin outside; no one knew how they were made. There was one school of thought that believed they grew that way.

Caroline :

Gingerbread-men are easy to make and so pretty. You can tie ribbon round their necks and stick tiny sweets on as buttons.

Charles :

Don't the little pets eat the ribbon?

Emmeline :

Don't be silly, Charles. What are nannies for but to prevent such goings-on? Caroline, what do I do about milk?

Caroline :

All children bring their own nowadays, along with their shoes and comb. There's a good bit of bragging done by the nannies who have Grade A, or whose employers keep cows.

Charles :

Yes, I can imagine them playing off a herd of Jerseys against a Rolls. What is considered the smartest fun for after tea?

Caroline :

After tea there are two courses open to you. Either you give each child a present and leave them to play with each other's or you hire an entertainer. I am rather in favour of the first course. A conjuror's best tricks are always wasted on very small children—they only really like the part right at the end when the whirls of coloured paper and the rabbit appear. A cinema frightens most of them but they'd simply adore an old-fashioned magic lantern, especially if some of the slides got put in upsidedown, but it's hard to find a professional entertainer who will deign to use one now. I've often thought that somewhere there must be a very old gentleman lovingly fingering slides of the

Fairy Bluebell and Auntie at the Seaside and yearning to conjure again that peculiar smell of hot tin. Perhaps Punch and Judy is the best fun. The hangman and the skeleton have no horrid significance for the very young and they howl with joy at the crocodile. If you decide on presents and no entertainer, don't bother to choose personal toys for each child because, in any case, they'll all want each other's. Get three different kinds and then they can just swop round. But don't forget to buy a few extra ones as some always get smashed and no one cares for the humiliation of going home with a toy that won't work. At about six-fifteen, you have ice-cream and lemonade. This is a sign that the party is expiring.

Charles :

Like being offered a second cup of tea by a Chinese.

Caroline :

Just the same. When the last ice is finished off, moist and sweet in the saucer, the muslin dresses and sailor-suits troop away—to return, muffled to the tips of their ears, amid a faint buzzing of ' Say-thank-you-for-a-nice-party '. Then the faces like flowers are turned up for kisses and, for a moment you are in another world, a world where ice-cream is the ultimate prize and all flesh is soft and cool as a violet petal. . . . I adore children's parties! Everyone is wildly enthusiastic; they have the nicest manners and get every bit of stimulus they need from asking each other's names and ages.

Emmeline :

Sweet Caroline, given all our talents I don't see how both our parties can help being wonderful successes!

Charles :

One thing we've all forgotten about is the guests. They do perform a certain function, you know. Get the list, Caroline, and let's see whom Henry's asked. My God! he's got the Fox-Vermins down! Poor Caroline, if there is one couple calculated to wreck any party. . . .

Round the Fire

DRAW UP A CHAIR and make yourself comfortable if, like us, you are not in the mood for a round of boisterous party games. But we *would* like something with which to 'animate an hour of vacant ease'. Perhaps someone has a good story to tell, or maybe a gentle little quiz might help to sharpen up our wits.

But don't begin to rack your brains just yet. For between the covers of this book may be found the means of passing several idle moments in company round the fireside. A ghost story, for instance, which is clamouring to be read aloud, will be found in the section entitled 'Christmas Reading' (on page 156); and, in the same section, there is another tale which, for greatest effect, should be retailed by a woman (page 130).

'Scrapbooks' (page 194) provide two specialised questionnaires in the shape of a Ghost Quiz and a Christmas Catechism.

And here, to keep the more restless souls from slipping too far back into their chairs and assuming an altogether indecorous attitude, is a random selection of sense and nonsense. Don't trouble to fetch a pencil and paper—they are not required; nor need any member of the company leave the room to enable the rest to conspire. Any exertion necessary is entirely mental. (Where answers are required, they will be found in Appendix 1, page 258.)

SWIFT WORK

The following 'verse', made up entirely of Latin words, is attributed to Dean Swift. By allowing for the false spelling, and running the words into each other, the passage may be read so that it makes good sense in English!

> Mollis abuti,
> Has an acuti,
> No lasso finis,
> Molli divinis.
> Omi de armis tres,
> Imi na dis tres,
> Cantu disco ver
> Meas alo ver?

Here is an extract from the consultation of four physicians on a nobleman who was dying:

1ST DOCTOR: Is his honor sic? Prae laetus felis pulse. It do es beat veris loto de.

2ND DOCTOR: No notis as qui cassi e ver fel tu metri it. Inde edit is as fastas an alarum, ora fire bellat nite.

3RD DOCTOR: It is veri hei!

4TH DOCTOR: Noto contra dictu, in my juge mentitis veri loto de. It is as orto maladi, sum callet.

FOR SERVICES RENDERED

Bills addressed to oneself do not normally make very amusing reading; but the invoice of the Cirencester painter, mentioned by Bishop Horne (*Essays and Thoughts*), must have brought a smile even to the face of the recipient. This is how it was set out:

> Mr. Charles Terrebee
> To Joseph Cook, Dr.
> To mending the Commandments, altering the Belief, and making a new Lord's Prayer .. £1 1 0

And here is a carpenter's bill of the fifteenth century:

	s.	d.
Item. To screwynge a horne on $\frac{8}{7}$ Devil, and glueinge a bitt on hys tayle		vij
Item. To repayring $\frac{8}{7}$ Vyrginne Marye before and behind, and makynge a new Chylde	ij	viij

SPEAKING OF THAT

Can you make sense out of this perfectly grammatical sentence?

The gentleman said in speaking of the word that that that that that that lady parsed was not that that that that gentleman had asked her to analyse.

KNOW ANYTHING?

1. What is the county town of:
   (a) Westmorland?
   (b) Rutland?
   (c) Cornwall?
   (d) Sussex?

2. And the capital of:
   (a) Thailand?
   (b) Mexico?
   (c) Union of South Africa?
   (d) Nicaragua?

3. And anyway, where is:
   (a) Thailand?
   (b) Nicaragua?
   (c) Timbuctoo?
   (d) Little Snoring?

4. Who said or wrote:
   (a) To gild the lily?
   (b) A little knowledge is a dangerous thing?
   (c) Lead on, Macduff?
   (d) Britannia rules the waves?

5. What is the difference (if any) between a:
   (a) Bibliopole?
   (b) Bibliomane?
   (c) Bibliophile?
   (d) Bibliopegist?

6. What is the modern name for:
   (*a*) Eboracum?
   (*b*) Byzantium?
   (*c*) Brighthelmstone?
   (*d*) Verulam?

SPANISH GOSSIP

Here is a game which should have the effect of curbing the activities of the confirmed gossip-mongers.

Somebody thinks of a sentence— 'Janet's got a red nose' would do nicely—and passes it on, in a whisper, to his neighbour. She (naturally!) immediately whispers her version into the ear of the person sitting next to her, and so on right round the circle. No one may ask for the words to be repeated: they must accept them as they come.

Eventually the sentence comes back to plague the inventor. And, you can believe it or not, it will probably reach him as 'Arthur's got false teeth'. Try it and see.

THE ANSWER'S A LEMON

Let someone think of a word, denoting a class of people or thing, of not fewer than four letters, e.g., 'Pear'. Now a second person must have a fruit whose initial letter is the same as the final letter of the word *pear*. If, for example, he says 'Raspberry' he will no doubt be setting quite a knotty problem to his next-door neighbour. The latter might, of course, reply with 'Yam', but as this contains fewer than four letters (and plurals not being admissible) he would have to think again—hard!

No one should be allowed more than one minute in which to produce a word, and the same word must not be introduced twice. Failure to comply with the rules means that the player drops out of the game.

BISHOP WILBERFORCE'S PUZZLE

The answer to this riddle may not be hard to seek; but can you name the components of which the whole is made up?

All pronounce me a wonderful piece of mechanism, and yet few people have numbered the strange medley of which I am composed. I have a large box and two lids, two caps, two musical instruments, a number of weathercocks, three established measures, some weapons of warfare, and a great many little articles that carpenters cannot do without; then I have about me a couple of esteemed fishes, and a great many of a smaller kind; two lofty trees, and the fruit of an indigenous plant; a handsome stag, and a great number of a smaller kind of game; two halls or places of worship, two students or rather scholars, the stairs of an hotel, and half a score of Spanish gentlemen to attend on me. I have what is the terror of the slave, also two domestic animals, and a number of negatives.

THE LAST WORD

Whose last words were these?
1. I feel the daisies growing over me.
2. It is small, very small indeed.
3. It matters little how the head lieth.
4. All my possessions for a moment of time.
5. It is not my design to drink or sleep, but my design is to make what haste I can to be gone.
6. Oh, my country! How I leave my country!
7. Let the light enter.
8. Let not poor Nelly starve.

THE GREAT PANJANDRUM

The following nonsense was written by Samuel Foote to test the memory of Charles Macklin, the actor, whose proud boast it was that he could repeat anything after reading or hearing it once:

She went into the garden to cut a cabbage to make an apple pie. Just then, a great she-bear coming down the street poked its nose into the shop-window. 'What! No soap?' So he died, and she very imprudently married the barber. And there were present at the wedding the Jobilillies, and the Piccannies, and the Garyulies, and the great Panjandrum himself, with the little button on top. So they all fell to playing catch-as-catch-can, till the gunpowder ran out of the heels of their boots.

LETTER PERFECT?

1. Luke had it first; Paul had it last; boys never have it; girls have it but once; Miss Sullivan had it twice in the same place, but when she married Pat Murphy she never had it again. What is it?
2. Spell brandy in three letters.
3. Why is the letter R most important to young people?
4. Why is the letter E like London?
5. I am neither flesh, fish nor fowl, yet I frequently stand upon one leg; if you behead me I stand upon two; if you again decapitate me, I stand upon four. What am I?
6. What letter is most pleasing to a deaf woman?
7. Give two words in which the five vowels follow each other in their proper order.

LOCAL COLOUR

We once knew a man who was able to pronounce the name of that truly remarkable place in Wales which begins with Llanfair-something and goes on almost indefinitely. Even if you do know how to pronounce it, there is scarcely time to go into all that now. Instead, perhaps you will say how the local inhabitants pronounce:

(a) Leominster.
(b) Methwold.
(c) Wymondham (Leicester).
(d) Wymondham (Norfolk).
(e) Launceston (Cornwall).
(f) Carshalton.
(g) Portishead.
(h) Cirencester.
(i) Kirkcudbright.
(j) Dalziel.
(k) Strachan.
(l) Cockburnspath.

CHESTNUTS

1. Why is a mouse when it spins (but seriously)?
2. Why is a raven like a writing desk?
3. A tall, dark Yorkshireman with a walrus moustache travelled from Wigan to Ashby-de-la-Zouch on a wet Wednesday night in February. His name was Bodger. Why?
4. How many months in the year have thirty days?
5. What's the difference between a turkey with one wing and a turkey with two?
6. Why does a tall man eat less Christmas dinner than a short one?
7. What is it which never was seen, felt, nor heard; never was, and never will be, and yet has a name?
8. What is most like a cat looking out of a window?
9. What word is it that is made shorter by adding another syllable to it?
10. When is a horse like a fish?

11. Why is a busy-body like a cat on the roof of a fish-monger's shop?

12. Don Pedro went to buy a mule. After much haggling the horse dealer agreed to let Don Pedro have the mule for 100 pesetas if he were allowed to purchase the mule's first-born at ten per cent the price of the mule plus a peseta for the number of days in the month in which the mule foaled. If the mule foaled in March, how much would Don Pedro receive?

CHARADES

My FIRST's a little busy thing,
My SECOND ladies do
Impelled by love their flight to wing;
My WHOLE—say, what are you?
An animal of swiftest pace,
Endowed with beauty, strength and
grace.

My FIRST is of illustrious line,
Of beauteous form and face divine;
Which when my SECOND does assail,
Both form and beauty then do fail;
My WHOLE an arduous task to do
With wives who hoity-toity ways pursue.

NO JIGGERY-POKERY!

Just as a matter of interest, how many words like ' hocus-pocus ' and ' namby-pamby ' can you think of in, say, five minutes? The words must conform to this construction, i.e., rhymed words with different initial letters.

And while we are at it, how must a circle be drawn round a person placed in the centre of a room, so that he will not be able to jump out of it though his legs are free?

ASK ME ANOTHER

1. What does ' Christmas ' mean in rhyming slang?
2. What do you understand by ' first footing '?
3. Why is the holly bush so called?
4. Why did Shakespeare entitle one of his plays *Twelfth Night*?
5. When was Christmas on New Year's Day?
6. When did January 1st become New Year's Day?

PEU DE CHOSE ET PRESQUE TROP

La vie est vaine:
　Un peu d'amour,
Un peu de haine . . .
　Et puis—bonjour!

La vie est brève:
　Un peu d'espoir,
Un peu de rêve . . .
　Et puis—*bonsoir!*

Scrapbooks

1

A CHRISTMAS ALBUM

ENTER THE HERO

Why, gentlemen, do you know what you do? ha! would you have kept me out? CHRISTMAS, old Christmas, Christmas of London, and Captain Christmas? Pray you, let me be brought before my lord chamberlain, I'll not be answered else: *'Tis merry in hall, when beards wag all*: I have seen the time you have wish'd for me, for a merry Christmas; and now you have me, they would not let me in: *I must come another time!* a good jest, as if I could come more than once a year. Why, I am no dangerous person, and so I told my friends of the guard. I am old Gregory Christmas still, and though I am come out of Pope's Head Alley, as good a Protestant as any in my parish.

From *A Masque of Christmas* by Ben Jonson (1616).

194

LET US BE GAY

So now is come our joyfull'st feast;
  Let every man be jolly;
Each room with ivy leaves is drest,
  And every post with holly.

George Wither (1588-1667).

A TOAST IN LAMB'S WOOL

The Wassail Bowl was sometimes composed of ale instead of wine; with nutmeg, sugar, toast, ginger, and roasted crabs; in this way the nut-brown beverage is still prepared in some old families, and round the hearths of substantial farmers at Christmas. It is also called Lamb's Wool, and is celebrated by Herrick in his *Twelfth Night*:

> ' Next crowne the bowle full
>   With gentle Lamb's Wool;
> Add sugar, nutmeg, and ginger,
>   With store of ale too;
>   And thus ye must doe
> To make the Wassaile a swinger.'

The custom of drinking out of the same cup gave place to each having his cup. When the steward came to the door with the Wassel, he was to cry three times, *Wassel, Wassel, Wassel,* and then the chappell (chaplein) was to answer with a song.

From *Archaeologia.*

BIRD SONG AT NIGHT

Some say that ever 'gainst that season comes
Wherein our Saviour's birth is celebrated,
The bird of dawning singeth all night long;
And then, they say, no spirit can walk abroad;
The nights are wholesome; then no planets strike,
No fairy takes, no witch hath power to charm;
So hallow'd and so gracious is the time.

William Shakespeare (1564-1616).

FROM MARMION

Heap on more wood! The wind is chill;
But let it whistle as it will,
We'll keep our Christmas merry still . . .

England was merry England, when
Old Christmas brought his sports again.
'Twas Christmas broached the mightiest ale;
'Twas Christmas told the merriest tale;
A Christmas gambol oft could cheer
The poor man's heart through half the year.

Sir Walter Scott (1771-1832).

AIR MINISTRY, NOTE

If Christmas day on Thursday be,
A windy winter ye shall see,
Windy weather in each week,
And hard tempest strong and thick;
The summer shall be good and dry,
Corn and beasts shall multiply.

From an old almanack.

YULETIDE SUPERSTITIONS

If one would go to the crossroads between eleven and twelve on Christmas Day, and listen, he would hear what most concerns him in the coming year.

On Christmas Eve thrash the garden with a flail, with only a shirt on, and the grass will grow well next year.

If a shirt be spun, woven and sewed by a pure, chaste maiden on Christmas Day, it will be proof against lead or steel.

If one is born at sermon time on Christmas morning, he will possess the power to see spirits.

The ashes of the Christmas log were supposed to give fertility to the ground, to rid cattle of vermin, to cure toothache and to protect the house from fire and ill-luck.

If a girl knocked loudly at the sty door on Christmas Eve and a great hog grunted in reply, her predestined husband would be an old man; if it was a little pig, that gave promise of a young one.

USEFUL ADVICE

At Christmas play and make good
    cheer,
For Christmas comes but once a
    year.
At Christmas be merry and thank
    God for all,
And feast thy poor neighbour, the
    great with the small.

From *Hundreth Good Poyntes of Husbandrie*
by Thomas Tusser (1557).

SAUSAGE AND STRONG BEER

An English gentleman, at the opening of the great day (i.e. on Christmas Day in the morning), had all his tenants and neighbours enter his hall by daybreak. The strong beer was broached, and the black-jacks went plentifully about with toast, sugar, and nutmeg, and good Cheshire cheese.

The Hackin (the great sausage) must be boiled by daybreak or else two young men must take the maiden (i.e. the cook) by the arms, and run her round the market-place till she is shamed of her laziness.

From *Round About Our Sea Coal Fire.*

OLD CUSTOMS ARE BEST

In modern times mistletoe was abandoned in the Christmas decking of churches, together with kissing at the services, because both were found to set the young ladies and gentlemen a-reading of the marriage service. Holly was substituted for the kisses and mistletoe, to indicate to them the dark monotony of matrimony and the numerous thorns with which it abounds.

FOR A CHRISTMAS CARD

Wake from thy nest, Robin-red-breast,
    Sing birds, in every furrow;
And from each hill, let music shrill
    Give my fair Love good-morrow!

Thomas Heywood (d. 1649).

PEACOCK PIE

The peacock was anciently in great demand for stately entertainments. Sometimes it was made into a pie, at one end of which the head appeared above the crust, in all its plumage, with the beak richly gilt; at the other end the tail was displayed. Such pies were served up at the solemn banquets of chivalry, when knights-errant pledged themselves to undertake any perilous enterprise; whence came the ancient oath, used by Justice Shallow, ' by cock and pie '.

The peacock was also an important dish for the Christmas feast; and Massinger, in his *City Madam*, gives some idea of the extravagance with which this, as well as other dishes, was prepared for the revels of an age which knew not ' rationing ':

' Men may talk of country Christ-
    masses:
Their thirty-pound butter'd eggs,
    their pies of carps' tongues,
Their pheasants drench'd with
    ambergris; the carcases
Of three fat wethers bruised for
    gravy, to
Make sauce for a single peacock;
    yet their feasts
Were fasts, compared with the
    city's.'

SNAPDRAGON

' This sport is seldom exhibited but in winter, and chiefly at Christmas time: it is simply heating of brandy, or some other ardent spirit, in a dish with raisins; when, the brandy being set on fire, the young folk of both sexes, standing round it, pluck out the raisins, and eat them as hastily as they can, but rarely without burning their hands, or scolding their mouths' (Strutt). It is usual to extinguish the lights in the room while the game is in progress.

Alice, it will be remembered, encountered a *Snapdragon-fly* through the looking-glass. Its body was 'made of plum-pudding, its wings of holly leaves and its head is a raisin burning in brandy'.

'And what does it live on?' Alice asked . . .

'Frumenty and mince pie . . . and it makes its nest in a Christmas box.'

FROM *IN MEMORIAM*

The time draws near the birth of
    Christ;
  The moon is hid, the night is still;
  The Christmas bells from hill to hill
Answer each other in the mist.

But they my troubled spirit rule,
  For they controll'd me when a boy;
  They bring me sorrow touched with
    joy
The merry merry bells of Yule.

      Alfred, Lord Tennyson (1809–1892).

A SALUTARY LESSON

In the Tyrolean Alps it is believed that the cattle have the gift of Language on Christmas Eve. But it is a sin to attempt to play the eavesdropper on them. An Alpine story is told of a farmer's servant who did not believe that the cattle could speak, and, to make sure, he hid in his master's stable on Christmas Eve and listened. When the clock struck twelve he was surprised at what he heard. 'We shall have hard work to do this day week,' said one horse. 'Yes, the farmer's servant is heavy,' answered the other horse. 'And the way to the churchyard is long and steep,' said the first. The servant was buried that day week.

CHRISTMAS EVE

The minstrels played their Christ-
  mas tune
Tonight beneath my cottage eaves;
While smitten by a lofty moon,
The encircling laurels, thick with
  leaves,
Gave back a rich and dazzling
  sheen,
That overpowered their natural
  green!
      William Wordsworth (1770–1850).

MEMORY OF CHILDHOOD[1]

Oh, I remember now
A dell of snow
Frost on the bough;
None there but I:
Snow, snow, and a wintry sky.
      Walter de la Mare (b. 1873).

THE YULE LOG

The Yule clog is a great log of wood, sometimes the root of a tree, brought into the house with great ceremony, on Christmas Eve, laid in the fireplace, and lighted with the brand of last year's clog. While it lasted, there was great drinking, singing, and telling of tales. Sometimes it was accompanied by Christmas candles; but in the cottages the only light was from

[1] Quoted by permission of the author and Messrs. Faber and Faber.

the ruddy blaze of the great wood fire. The Yule clog was to burn all night; if it went out, it was considered a sign of ill-luck. Herrick mentions it in one of his songs:

> ' Come, bring with a noise,
> My merrie, merrie boyes,
> The Christmas log to the firing;
> While my good dame, she
> Bids ye all be free,
> And drink to your heart's desiring.'

There were several superstitions connected with it among the peasantry. If a squinting person come to the house while it was burning, or a person barefooted, it was considered an ill-omen. The brand remaining from the Yule clog was carefully put away to light the next year's Christmas fire.

SONG FOR MERRY CHRISTMAS

Now Christmas soon will come again,
   And everybody knows it,
Make yourself merry while you can,
   If you have the means to do it.
I'll tell you of things that you may see,
   When you're about the town,
And if you have got any money to
      spend
   I hope you'll lay out a brown—
      brown—brown.

Now Christmas as it will soon arrive,
   Let's hope each hungry sinner,
Will have a good big lump of beef,
   And a pudding for his dinner.

Street Ballad (early 19th century).

DISSENTIENT VOICE

Glorious time of great too much!
Too much heat and too much noise,
Too much babblement of boys,
Too much eating, too much drinking,
Too much everything but thinking.

Leigh Hunt (1784–1859).

ONCE UPON A TIME

A man might then behold
   At Christmas, in each hall,
Good fires to curb the cold,
   And meat for great and small.
The neighbours were friendly bidden,
   And all had welcome true,
The poor from the gates were not
      chidden,
   When this old cap was new.

Thomas Hood (1779–1845).

CAROL

I sing of a maiden
That is makéles:
King of all kings
To her son she ches.

He came al so stillé
There his moder was,
As dew in Aprillé
That falleth on the grass.

He came al so stillé
To his moderes bour,
As dew in Aprillé
That falleth on the flour.

He came al so stillé
There his moder lay,
As dew in Aprillé
That falleth on the spray.

Moder and maiden
Was never none but she:
Well may such a lady
Godé's moder be.

Anonymous (14th century).

ALL THAT REMAINS

But is old, old, good old Christmas gone? Nothing but the hair of his good, grey, old head and beard left? Well, I will have that, seeing I cannot have more of him.

Hue and Cry after Christmas.

A CHRISTMAS CATECHISM

1. *When was Christmas first celebrated?*

2. *When was Christmas forbidden in this country?*

3. *Do you know why we have:*
   (i) Candles on a Christmas tree:
   (ii) Christmas waits: (iii) Kissing under the mistletoe?

4. *What was the nationality of:*
   (i) Santa Claus: (ii) Good King Wenceslas: (iii) Harlequin and Columbine?

5. *In what country is it a Christmas custom to:*
   (i) Hang evergreen wreaths over the front door: (ii) Spread hay under the cloth at dinner: (iii) Have a traditional round yeast cake filled with nuts, raisins, and spices?

6. *When is:*
   (i) Twelfth Night: (ii) 'The Feast of Stephen': (iii) Hogmanay?

7. *Who wrote:*
   (i) 'Christmas Holiday': (ii) 'A Christmas Carol': (iii) 'Christmas Day in the Workhouse'?

8. *What do you understand by:*
   (i) Snapdragon: (ii) Christmas Roses: (iii) Frumenty?

9. *Why are these so-called:*
   (i) Boxing Day: (ii) Wassailing: (iii) The Magi?

10. *What is the origin of:*
    (i) The Yule Log: (ii) The boar's head: (iii) Turkey and sausages?

11. *Do you know the name of a:*
    (i) King of England crowned on Christmas Day: (ii) Modern playwright born near Christmas: (iii) Child of our Royal Family born on Christmas Day?

12. *In what Christmas plays do these characters occur:*
    (i) Captain Hook: (ii) Saint George: (iii) Tyltyl?

13. *Who composed the:*
    (i) Dance of the Sugar-Plum Fairy: (ii) Christmas Concerto: (iii) Christmas Oratorio?

14. *Three lines from Christmas Carols: what is the preceding line:*
    (i) '... Let nothing you dismay': (ii) '... Bearing gifts we traverse afar': (iii) '... And to you your wassail, too'?

Answers in Appendix 2, page 259.

A BEVY OF BOGEYS

DON'T LOOK NOW!

Like one, that on a lonesome road
  Doth walk in fear and dread,
And having once turned round walks
    on,
  And turns no more his head;
Because he knows, a frightful fiend
  Doth close behind him tread.

      Samuel Taylor Coleridge (1772–1834).

WHAT A PERFORMANCE!

November 2 (1649) came something
into the Withdrawing Room, treading
as they conceived, much like a bear,
which first only walked about a
quarter of an hour; at length it made
a noise about the Table, and threw
the Warming-Pan so violently that it
quite spoiled it. It threw also Glass
and great Stones at them again, and
the Bones of Horses and all so violently, that the Bedstead and Walls were
bruised by them. This night they set
Candles all about the Rooms, and
made fires up to the Mantle-trees of
the Chimneys, but all were put out,
no body knew how . . . the Curtains
torn with the Rods from their Beds,
and the Bed-Posts pulled away, that
the Tester fell down upon them, and
the feet of the Bed-stead cloven in
two. And upon the Servants in the
Truckle-bed, who lay, all this time,
sweating with fear, there was first a
little, which made them begin to stir,
but before they could get out, there
came a whole Cowl, as it were, of
stinking Ditch-water down upon them,
so green, that it made their Shirts and
Sheets of that colour too.

From *More Remarkable and True Stories o
Apparitions and Witchcraft*, by Henry More,
D.D. (1688).

LAUGH THAT OFF

One of the nastiest things to have
happen to you is to reach out your hand
in the dark to grope for the matches and
have the box thrust into your fingers.

OFF THE RATION

The light falls upon the face. It is perfectly white, perfectly bloodless. The eyes look like polished tin; the lips are drawn back and the principal feature next to those dreadful eyes is the teeth, like those of some wild animal, hideously, glaringly white and fanglike. It approaches the bed with a strange gliding movement, clashing together the long nails that literally appear to hang from the finger ends. The church clock proclaims the hour of one: a hissing sound comes from the throat of the hideous being and he raises his long gaunt arms—the lips move. He advances and with a sudden rush that could not be foreseen—with a strange howling cry that was enough to awaken terror in every breast—the figure seized her long tresses and held her to the bed. With a plunge, he seizes her neck in his fang-like teeth— a gush of blood and . . . *the vampyre is at his hideous repast!*

From *Varney the Vampire or the Feast of Blood,* by Thomas Preskett Prest (1847).

TO RAISE THE DEAD

. . . . Wizards know their times:
Deep night, dark night, the silent of
    the night,
The time of night when Troy was set
    on fire;
The time when screech-owls cry, and
    ban-dogs howl,
And spirits walk, and ghosts break up
    their graves,—
That time best fits the work we have
    in hand.

      William Shakespeare (1564-1616).

GHASTLY GOINGS ON!

. . . All was quiet for a little time while we were in the Chamber with a Light, but we were no sooner out of the Chamber with the Candle but the noise under the Bed, tugging of the Mat, pulling of the Bedclothes began again. Moreover, something came into the Bed, which the Gentlewoman said ran upon her by degrees and seemed little and soft like a Mole. Upon this she skreekt out, and we came in again with the Candle, then all was still again.

From *Sadducismus Triumphatus or Full and Plain Evidence concerning Witches and Apparitions,* by Joseph Glanvill (1681).

A TOUCH BEHIND THE EARS

Anno 1670, not far from Cyrencester, was an Apparition. Being demanded, whether a good spirit or bad, returned no answer, but disappeared with a curious Perfume and a most melodious Twang. Mr. W. Lillie believes it was a Fairie.

      John Aubrey (1626-1697).

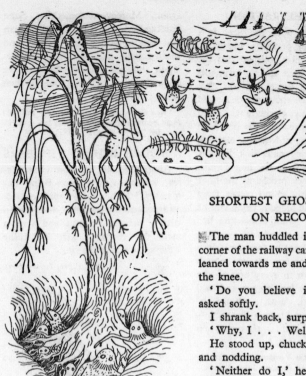

SHORTEST GHOST STORY
ON RECORD

The man huddled in the opposite corner of the railway carriage suddenly leaned towards me and tapped me on the knee.

'Do you believe in ghosts?' he asked softly.

I shrank back, surprised.

'Why, I . . . Well, no.'

He stood up, chuckling to himself and nodding.

'Neither do I,' he croaked—and vanished.

IN TOWN TONIGHT

A little ere the mightiest Julius fell,
The graves stood tenantless and the
    sheeted dead
Did squeak and gibber in the
    Roman streets.

William Shakespeare (1564-1616).

POUR CHASSER LES
MAUVAIS ESPRITS

St. Francis and St. Benedight
Blesse this house from wicked wight;
From the night-mare and the goblin
That is hight good fellow Robin:
Keep it from all evil spirits,
Fairies, weezels, rats and ferrets:
    From curfew time
    To the next prime.

FROM DEATH'S JEST BOOK

What dost thou strain above her
    Lovely throat's whiteness?
A silken chain, to cover
    Her bosom's brightness?
Tremble and weep not: what dost
    thou fear?
    —My blood is spilt like wine,
Thou hast strangled and slain me,
    lover,
    Thou hast stabbed me, dear,
      In the ghosts' moonshine.
    Is that the wind? No, no;
    Only her goblin doth blow
    Through the murderer's ribs to
      and fro,
      In its own moonshine.

Thomas Lovell Beddoes (1803–1849).

THE GOBLIN MEN

One had a cat's face,
One whisked a tail,
One tramped at a rat's pace,
One crawled like a snail,
One like a wombat prowled obtuse
and furry,
One like a ratel tumbled hurry-
skurry.

Christina Rossetti (1830–1894).

FROM THE APOCRYPHA

There be spirits that are created for vengeance, which in their fury lay on sore strokes; in the time of destruction they pour out their force, and appease the wrath of him that made them.

Ecclesiasticus xxxix, 28.

THE GHOST GAME

The game is played with a table, preferably round and with a polished surface. The other necessities are a glass tumbler and twenty-six small pieces of paper, each marked with a letter of the alphabet. Set the letters in a circle round the table with the glass turned downwards in the centre. The players sit round and each places the right fore-finger on the base of the glass. After a moment or two the proper mood should be established for contact with the Other World and the player who is to act as master of ceremonies asks a question. Simple— and not too flippant—questions requiring a straight yes or no or a single, short word reply are best at first. Repeat the question as necessary until the tumbler begins to move. When it does, all fingers should remain in position, resting lightly on the base and following — not guiding — the motion of the glass as it swings from letter to letter spelling out the answer. If it jumbles, try again. The author of this scrapbook, who, like most other people, doesn't believe in ghosts, but is frightened to death of them, assures the sceptical that this method of invoking the Spirits fails very rarely indeed.

BRIEF ENCOUNTER

The other day, upon the stair,
I met a man who wasn't there.
He wasn't there again today—
I wish that man would go away!

Source, unfortunately, unknown.

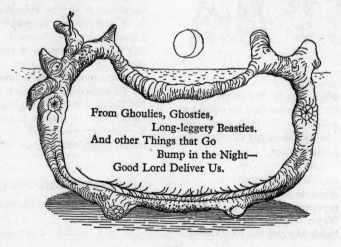

From Ghoulies, Ghosties,
Long-leggety Beasties.
And other Things that Go
Bump in the Night—
Good Lord Deliver Us.

203

WHO'S WHAT IN THE SPIRIT WORLD

(1) VARIOUS APPARITIONS.
What kind of a ghost would you expect to : (i) Shriek and hurl things about. (ii) Haunt graveyards and eat dead bodies. (iii) Visit you in your own likeness. (iv) Write under another man's name?

(2) FIRESIDE PHANTOMS.
Who wrote these macabre masterpieces : (i) Green Tea. (ii) A Warning to the Curious. (iii) The Turn of the Screw. (iv) The Willows?

(3) DEMON'S DIARY.
When is : (i) Walpurgis Night. (ii) The proper time for a ghost to go home. (iii) Hallowe'en. (iv) The propitious day to contact the Little People?

(4) CELLULOID SPECTRES.
Name the films in which these actors impersonated ghosts: (i) Naunton Wayne. (ii) Kay Hammond. (iii) Frank Morgan. (iv) Noel Coward.

(5) CREEPY CONVERSATIONS.
Who were the ghosts addressed here : (i) ' Be thou a spirit of health or goblin damn'd? ' (ii) ' There's more of gravy than grave about you, whatever you are! ' (iii) ' Why, I will see thee at Philippi then.' (iv) ' Avaunt! And quit my sight! '?

(6) NATIVE HAUNTS.
What is the native origin of : (i) A banshee. (ii) A dybbuk. (iii) A zombi. (iv) A kelpie?

(7) HOUSEHOLD HINTS.
What precautions would you take : (i) To keep vampires out of your bedroom. (ii) Before digging a mandrake root. (iii) To protect yourself when invoking Black Spirits. (iv) To keep on friendly terms with the local fairies?

(8) KNOW YOUR SPOOKS.
(i) Is LYCANTHROPY (*a*) A school for sorcerers. (*b*) The study of disembodied spirits. (*c*) The transformation of a witch into a wolf?
(ii) Is THE SPOOK SONATA (*a*) Music played at Witches' Sabbaths. (*b*) A play by Strindberg. (*c*) A composition suggested to Paganini during a nightmare?
(iii) Would a ghost use a PLANCHETTE (*a*) To write with. (*b*) To wrap round itself like a shroud. (*c*) To make itself invisible?
(iv) Would a WARLOCK (*a*) Haunt battlefields. (*b*) Invoke demons. (*c*) Grow in graveyards?
Answers in Appendix 3, page 260.

COMFORTING THOUGHT

Ghosts never appear on Christmas Eve.

Old proverb.

People throw stones only at trees with fruit on them

It is as much intemperance to weep too much as to laugh too much

A good grievance is worth more than bad pay

A Christmas Bill

BY NATHANIEL GUBBINS

MINISTRY OF SELF-DEFENCE
Being a Bill

To be presented before the House of Parliament in the Nest, to make provision to excuse and exonerate N. Gubbins, Esq., journalist, of the Nest, in the County of Surrey, from all organised Christmas festivities in the year 1947 and thereafter; and from the responsibility of providing a turkey, goose (or ducks), or any other form of poultry, game or other food-stuffs known as Christmas cheer, within the meaning of the Bill, except that he will undertake to provide monies for the purchase of the said Christmas cheer by a third person.

BE IT ENACTED by and with the advice and consent of the ladies temporal, though not so spiritual, in the present Parliament assembled in the Nest, and by the authority of the same as follows:

1 *That it shall be lawful* for N. Gubbins, Esq., journalist, in the County of Surrey, to abstain from all Christmas entertainments, festivities and whoopee by his own free will and judgment and without Recrimination.

2 *That the said* N. Gubbins, Esq., shall not be asked at the last moment to purchase, if available, in the open or black market, or by any other means come by, a turkey, goose or any other foodstuffs known hereinafter as Christmas cheer, as it is well known to the ladies temporal of the said Parliament of the Nest that the said N. Gubbins, Esq., is a Fool, who, in the past, has not only been swindled by the licensed and unlicensed vendors of Christmas cheer, but by the vendors of all saleable commodities at all times in the year and at any time in his life.

It being well known also, not only to the ladies temporal, but to a large

206

number of his Most Excellent Majesty's subjects in the County of Surrey, that the said N. Gubbins, Esq., lost six Christmas turkeys in trains, omnibuses, taxicabs, telephone boxes, and other public vehicles and places in the years 1942, 1940, 1939, 1938, 1937 and 1936, and various other items of Christmas cheer in other years, he shall hereinafter be known as an Irresponsible Person unfit to negotiate, trade or make purchases in any market whatsoever.

3 *That it shall be unlawful* for the said N. Gubbins, Esq., to be coerced as a member of any Christmas shopping expedition, or as an escort to any such expedition, or detailed as a one-man fatigue party to any such expedition or expeditions.

It shall be unlawful also to expect him to

(*a*) Choose, select, have printed and post any Christmas card or cards to any person known as a friend or relative, unless of his own free will and judgment.

(*b*) Choose, select and purchase by divers means, and at great trouble and expense, any present, seasonable gift or gee-gaw, to be wrapped, tied with string, card or fancy twine and posted to any person known as a friend or relative, unless of his own free will and judgment.

(*c*) *It shall be lawful* for him to present or not to present, according to his own free will and judgment, such monies as he may deem advisable and within his means after deductions of income-tax, to such persons in lieu of the said presents, seasonable gifts or gee-gaws.

4 In the event of an invitation or invitations being received to attend a Christmas party or parties *it shall be lawful* for the said N. Gubbins, Esq., to say Yea or Nay to any one or all of such invitations.

It shall be unlawful also, in the event of the verdict being Nay, for any member of the Parliament of the Nest to make any attempt to reverse the verdict by persuasion, cajolery or mockery—to wit, by describing the said N. Gubbins, Esq., as Spoil-sport, Scrooge, or Sourpuss.

It shall be understood and lawful for any member of the said Parliament to attend, or not to attend, according to her wishes and free will, any party or parties, without escort and without let or hindrance.

5 In the unusual event of the verdict being Yea the said N. Gubbins, Esq., *shall have the* right to leave the party in a courteous manner at any time he thinks fit for any reason whatsoever, and shall be loyally supported in any lie, excuse or deception he may invent for that purpose.

It shall be understood also that there is no obligation on any other member of the Parliament of the Nest to leave at the same time; *that it is lawful* for them to leave at any time they think fit, singly, in pairs, or in groups, by any means available, on foot, by car, or in an ambulance, according to their condition.

6 *That it shall be lawful* to hold a party within the Nest itself, if provisions are available, and that any member of the Parliament of the Nest may invite to such a party any person who is not a convicted criminal, undischarged bankrupt or imbecile; *that it shall be lawful also* for any member of the Parliament of the Nest, and for N. Gubbins, Esq., to leave the party in a courteous manner and retire to bed at any time he or she thinks fit, providing always that each member shall be responsible for his or her own guest and not retire to bed until the said guest has departed.

7 *That it shall be unlawful* to place a paper cap or any other humorous headgear within the meaning of the Bill on the head of N. Gubbins, Esq., without his consent.

8 *That it shall be unlawful* to expect the said N. Gubbins, Esq., to pull more than two crackers after dinner or to read more than two humorous verses or to guess, or to attempt to guess, the answers to more than two funny riddles.

9 *That it shall be unlawful* to expect the said N. Gubbins, Esq., to play more than one game (each) of draughts, dominoes, halma, tiddley-winks, or snakes and ladders.

10 *That it shall be unlawful* to expect the said N. Gubbins, Esq., to tie small packages of decorations on any Christmas tree or trees; to fill and hang on a bedpost any stocking for any person over the age of ten years; to hang, nail, or otherwise suspend any part of any evergreen shrub or parasite plant (i.e. holly or mistletoe) in any part of the said

Nest or any other place; to sing songs, tell funny stories, give recitations or imitations, or make speeches; to dress up as any character, including the fictitious character of Father Christmas.

I I *It shall be understood* that Christmas is over at 24.00 hours precisely on the twenty-fifth day of December in the year 1947 and each subsequent year. The day after, beginning at 24.01 hours on the twenty-sixth day of December, or any time between 24.00 hours on the 25th December, and 24.01 hours on the 26th December, shall be known as Aspirin Day, when no festivities shall take place.

I2 *That this Bill* shall have three readings in the Nest and when, and if, passed by a majority shall become law and known hereinafter as THE DEFENCE OF N. GUBBINS, ESQ. (AT CHRISTMAS TIME) ACT.

This Christmas Business

BY ROY LEWIS

RASPBERRY JUICE may be a pleasant and even, in moderate quantities, a healthful drink; but it is not a profitable commercial investment. To make it a commercial proposition we must do a number of things to it, all worked out by years of business experience. First we must find it a name. For many purposes, it is advisable to depart entirely from the descriptive noun, and invent a name—such as Tono-Bungay—whereupon the need to include real (and expensive) raspberries in the formula also disappears. This is the procedure adopted by Hollywood when filming a novel. Let us suppose, however, that the connection with raspberries has a certain goodwill value, and call the commercially improved product ' Spirit of Raspberry '.

Our Advertising Consultants now launch an educational campaign. The press, hoardings, placards in the underground remind us that Raspberry Time is here again. Public Relations officers, those astounding men, induce newspaper editors to publish leading articles about Spirit of Raspberry, prominent authors to put it into incidents in their books, famous artists to paint pictures of it (for calendar manufacturers).

Our product is expensively packaged, and put up in liquid, powdered and capsule form in convenient sizes. The trade in extras is highly profitable. Everyone wants the copyright of our label. Patent medicine manufacturers want to be able to say ' tasteless when dissolved in Spirit of Raspberry '. Breakfast Food manufacturers want to be able to say ' serve with cream and Spirit of Raspberry '. The B.B.C. wants to do a script about it. In short, Spirit of Raspberry is now a national industry. It employs thousands and thousands of workpeople. It enters into imports and exports and, as a spirit, into the

Chancellor of the Exchequer's calculations. The Prime Minister imbibes it, Mr. Bernard Shaw denounces it. It causes untold inconvenience to the London Passenger Transport Board.

And all the time it is mere raspberry juice. Such is the power of prestige advertising, sentiment, and the profit-motive.

No single commercial enterprise has made a corner in Christmas, but Christmas as we know it is the product of a century of shrewd business development. Christmas has proved a sounder field for investment than railways or foreign Government bonds. It has proved a gold mine, an exhaustible gold mine of traditions, sentimentalities and superstitions wherewith to stimulate a totally fictitious demand for blatantly ephemeral merchandise.

It is no coincidence that the beginnings of the Christmas industry are to be found early in the industrial revolution. Christmas was a steadily increasing source of profit to the nineteenth century business man. Mr. Gradgrind had no use for Mr. Scrooge. Christmas was characteristically one of those hypocritical ways of getting rid of the periodic surpluses of capitalistic production which Mr. Marx, his stovepipe topper neatly stowed under his chair, was ruthlessly exposing in the British Museum in 1850. But even he, passionate moralist though he was, failed to expose the egregious deceits upon which Christmas extravagance was nourished, or prophesy the dimensions to which the traffic would grow. If Marx could have seen the Christmas shopping crowds of our day, the vast expenditure on presents, the fierce competition to market ' gifts that are different ', the heart taken out of the land to fatten turkeys, the children of the poor wailing lugubriously outside the doors of the *bourgeoisie*, the last mad scramble for tinsel and bits of pasteboard on December 24, the hectic gaiety that follows, and the utter stagnation and lethargy that supervenes, leading to a melancholy procession of ' Christmas sales—incredible reductions—prices slaughtered ', to what unforgettable picture of capitalist booms and slumps would he not have been inspired! He missed the chance. In a letter to Engels, dated December 25, 1857, his theme is exclusively the class struggle. Not even ironically did he convey the compliments of the season.

The build-up of Christmas, the creation of what is frankly called in the commercial parlance of dozens of branches of manufacturing ' the Christmas trade ' or ' the Christmas market ', was done with consummate skill. To the simple ceremonies ordained in the Christian year there were added a great many more of dubious antecedent, most of which were undoubtedly of purely pagan origin. The lustrations of the winter solstice were amalgamated with the Christian anniversary. The bells and the holly were brought together in a merger. The rediscovery of mistletoe and its uses by the early Victorians was a direct invitation to Sir James Frazer.

The fluxing agent used to bind the two traditions together was nostalgia. Railways were not enough for the Victorians; they must have the stage coach and the ' good old days ' also. They dragged in the yule logs. They yearned after the cosiness of ' merrie England ' and its warmhearted, uninhibited cheerfulness as hazily as we regret the security, certainty, sense of purpose and four-and-a-half per cent on gilt-edged of the Victorian age of gold. Conceivably they were more wilfully misled than we. Christmas, like most things, became for them an affair of paraphernalia, and paraphernalia costs money; they created Christmas in their own likeness. Just as the pre-raphaelites clothed their spruce if dreamy Arthurians in what looks suspiciously like fine cottons.

Nothing is so typical of this nostalgia than the legend of ' Christmas weather '. In the ' Good old times ' snow fell punctually at Christmas (which before 1752 itself fell on January 5th), icicles hung by the wall and there was skating at Dingley Dell. How did this money-making legend arise? Obviously, snow often does fall at Christmas—in Scandinavia, whence some choice Christmas customs reached us. Obviously, too, it does not fall in large areas of southern Europe where Christmas is as devoutly observed as anywhere else. It falls more often at Christmas on the Pennines and Snowdonia than in London. But, though our Christmas cards continue to depict stage coaches axle deep in snow, in our lifetimes, as we very well know, Christmas weather is a rarity. In the last fifty years there have been appreciable falls of snow in London at Christmas only three times—in 1906, 1927 and 1938. Even then it was less than six inches deep. Frost was more frequent; frosts at Christmas were recorded by the meteorological office in nearly one out of two years in the present century in Southern England, but only in six years did it permit skating in safety over the Christmas holiday. In point of fact, except for 1917, 1929, 1940–42 and 1946–47 winters have been exceedingly mild, and the snow has for the most part been supplied commercially in the form of cotton wool in shop window displays and other substances designed to impart the illusion of a dusting with hoar frost on seasonable gifts and decorations.

Records show, however, that before he was thirty Charles Dickens experienced six very severe Christmasses. Between 1782 and 1821 on no less than sixteen out of forty Christmasses, snow fell at Richmond, and the rest of the country suffered proportionately. Since it is the remarkable rather than the usual that is remembered, it is easy to understand why Dickens idealised the white Christmas under the impression that he was portraying the good old Christmas of the coaching days. During Victoria's reign, however, snow fell much less frequently than in Dickens' youth, though it was colder than we have generally known it. Before 1900 one out of every five Christmas spells had overall mean temperatures of 32 deg. F. or less, and in every other year at least one of the days in Christmas week had this temperature. Upon this imitation of Dickensian Christmas weather the Victorians built a prosperous Christmas industry, importing wholesale from Germany the customs of the good old days.

Commercial aspects of the traditional British Christmas were confined mainly to tipping. From waiters in coffee houses to civil servants, tipping at Christmas was the rule. Swift complained to Stella of the cost. The Foreign Office was asking for Christmas boxes until 1836. Bank clerks, even bank managers, were tipped up to the 'eighties. But it was the Victorians who developed the custom (brought from Germany) of giving ever more costly presents over an ever wider range of relatives at Christmas. For this purpose they first adopted the German Christmas tree, loaded with candles, sugar plums and Bavarian toys. In 1841 Albert delighted Viccy at Windsor with one of the first—it proved *gemütlich*—and Struwwelpeter popularised the tree so much that growing them for the trade became economic. Britain re-exported the Christmas tree craze to France, and in Paris alone 35,000 trees were being sold for Christmas *à l'anglais* at the close of the Empire. In turn, Britain imported from France the *bon-bon*, a Christmas sweet wrapped in tissue paper, and from it evolved the cracker, *bien sophistiqué*. First a *billet doux* was included in the wrapping, suitable for reading out under the mistletoe: then the enterprising manufacturer conceived the idea of imitating the crackle of the yule-log. To accommodate the explosive charge, the paper case had to be enlarged, which

in turn suggested the inclusion of expensive gifts instead of mere sweets
—hats, mottos, indoor fireworks, amulets, novelties for which the world
was scoured.

Next the Victorians seized on the Christmas stocking from the
Americans in the 'fifties. It was more capacious: you had to buy more
to fill it up. After a time it was sold in enormous quantities ready-
filled—in 1935 the custom lingered on in those terrible openwork
bootees filled with rubbishy 'novelties' whereof £43,000 worth
(ex-factory) were manufactured. From Germany again came the
lucrative myth of 'Father Christmas' *alias* St. Nicholas, *alias* Knecht
Rupprecht, who, according to Grimm (it would be Grimm) sometimes
appeared with the dwarf Krampus to carry off naughty children in his
sack. In Indiana, U.S.A., a township was named Santa Claus and has
flourished by reason of the enormous number of children who addressed
petitions simply to Santa Claus, creating large Post Office employment.
To the 600,000 annual begging letters, has, in recent times, been added

a vast Christmas catalogue mail from shops and businesses all over America, posted specially in Santa Claus, In., for the publicity value of the post mark. Violent land speculation duly developed, and a nice rake-off for the lawyers resulted from a recent lawsuit between Santa Claus of Santa Claus Inc., and Santa Claus Inc. Christmas novelty and toy factories are now under construction there.

The Christmas stocking and Father Christmas with his bulging sack were, however, long ago relegated to secondary importance; as early as 1850 a sound business instinct was encouraging children to select their own presents in Soho Bazaar, the Pantheon and Lowther Arcade. Father Christmas merely presided over well-planned forward purchasing operations—himself a victim of the casual labour problem. The time of huge parties, long lists of seasonable gifts, the ordering of vast quantities of food, drink and delicacies had arrived. Sideboards groaned, and the fifteen hours of Christmas Day were all too few to carry the load of new quaint customs and festivities, from snap-dragon to charades, which literary people dug up from old books, brought back in their carpet bags from their travels on the Continent or discovered in remote nooks of Cornwall or Cumberland and contributed through the pages of *Notes and Queries* to the common stock. Hard on their heels came the manufacturer who was able to supply Christmas cakes and puddings in airtight tins as early as 1875. Many of those who were making a good thing out of Christmas showed little scruple in their methods. ' Good King Wenceslas ', for example, was originally a Scandinavian spring song; His Majesty looked out on the feast of Easter, not Stephen. The song was altered to fit in to an anthology of Christmas carols, prepared for the trade.

Gradually almost every branch of commerce made money out of Christmas. The provision trades made everything from mince-pies to frumenty; the wine merchants put up bottles of rum punch in wassail packages; the tallow interests pushed fancy candles until the electrical gadget industry went one better; manufacturers of every kind purchased cheap paper and twisted it into expensive decorations; the black man on the Congo sweated to get the raw materials for coloured balloons; actors made money out of pantomime, conjurors out of children's parties, even the circus cashed in as a London Christmas attraction. In 1913 the daily papers ceased to publish over Christmas to mark the day's importance; long before that, magazines were cleaning up with special Christmas numbers twice as thick, twice as expensive, and (sometimes) charging twice the regular rate for advertisements. As the Empire expanded, manufacturers were able to combine the production of Christmas novelties with trade goods for the savages of Africa and Polynesia. The railways and the seaside resorts conspired together to get a slice of Christmas business. Nokes outdid Stokes in Christmas treats. . . .

A Ph.D. thesis could be written (and probably has been written) for the University of Arkansas on the Economic Implications of Christmas. We may only glance briefly at a few of the several completely new industries which the Spirit of Christmas has created. The Christmas card is another Victorian invention, designed to spread the obligation to spend money at Christmas far beyond the confines of one's immediate family. The first card is attributed to one Mr. W. M. Egley, who designed and etched it in the year 1842; it depicted a Roger de Coverley dance, along with other Christmas joys, in a genre reminiscent of the front cover of *Punch*.

Next year, J. C. Horsley, R.A., designed a card for Sir Henry Cole, K.C.B., which was reproduced by lithography. An edition of 1,000 coloured by hand was issued for public sale in 1846. By the 'sixties the Christmas card had begun to be an important part of the small tradesman's Christmas lines.

In 1937, 240,000,000 Christmas cards were sold in Britain, about twenty per family. The retail value must have been in the region of £3,000,000, and the post office must have collected around £500,000 in postage. Designers of Christmas cards before the war made £500 to £600 a year, and are now getting £1,000 to £1,500. One firm alone, out of over fifty concerned, introduced 3,000 new designs a year, everchanging variation on snow, frost, ice, mistletoe, holly, bells, stage coaches, black cats, angels, ships, yule logs, ye olden tymes, and such rather more loosely relevant subjects as the first Eton and Harrow match or the Taj Mahal. Vorticism and surrealism have inspired cards. The ribbons alone used to have a gross value of £100,000. A set of original Christmas verses was worth 7s. 6d. to 15s. depending on length, metre and lushness of sentiment; probably 10,000 new ones were wanted every year, or say an income of £350 a year for a dozen poets (how many make as much out of other sort of verse?) The paper shortage has notably cut into this valuable trade: in 1946 only 80,000,000 cards could be made, but their value was still about £2,500,000 owing to higher prices. Yet Christmas cards, though an abominable waste of time, temper and money, are a comparatively minor item in any family's Christmas budget.

We cannot follow in the same detail the Christmas cracker trade—which turns out 100,000,000 crackers in a good year—or the host of other vested interests concerned. The Census of Production (which valued cracker output in 1935 as £432,000—representing a retail trade of probably £1,000,000) is seriously at fault in not classifying this whole industry separately. The Capital tied up in Christmas can only be conjectured, but the annual turnover can be estimated with some approach to accuracy. Retail trade in Britain as a whole showed in December 1937 a forty per cent increase over the monthly average for the other eleven months. This is the measure of the Christmas trade. Sales of clothing were nearly fifty per cent greater in December. Household goods were nearly twenty-five per cent greater, food over

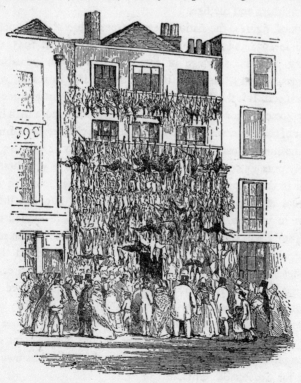

twenty per cent. At Christmas, of course, people eat more than usually expensive food; but only over a period of a week or ten days, and it is therefore difficult to resist the inference of these figures that during Christmas week people eat nearly half as much again in volume as in a normal week; or, if they concentrate their feasting into two or three days, these figures hint that they must eat perhaps two or three times their normal quantity of food. Of course, they cannot possibly enjoy it in the same ratio. The law of diminishing returns is inexorable. There may well be an actual disutility in eating so much more than usual (see an unpublished thesis for a doctorate of philosophy in the Faculty Library of the University of Arkansas). Perhaps the most revealing figure that can be quoted, however, is from the sales of British departmental stores. Sales of fancy goods, toys, novelties, sports and travel accessories were in pre-war years 200 per cent greater than in other months. That is what the Spirit of Christmas was worth to the purveyors of bookends, ashtrays, gift stationery, explosive cigars, bridge markers and the like.

In round figures, the nation's extra expenditure at Christmas-time reached in 1938 the tidy sum of £110,000,000; and in 1945, despite rationing and the shortage of raw materials which penalised the Christmas industry, the total, inflated by the rise in prices, was still £104,000,000. It is the merest guess that a trade of this magnitude would employ 400,000 people directly or indirectly, rather more than half the number of coal miners and twenty per cent of the civil servants. Immense capital resources must stand entrenched behind this vast business, which probably puts £5,000,000 annually into the pockets of shareholders.

Such is the colossus that modern commerce has made of Father Christmas and his sack. Rationing has slimmed him but little. It remains to be seen if the scientific, rationistic, neat-minded society of the future will reduce the strain he imposes on the public services by staggering him. Deep commercial cunning lies behind the two aphorisms 'Christmas comes but once a year' and 'Shop early for Christmas'. Sales resistance goes down helplessly before them. So great are the vested interests at work that it would be folly to hold out great hopes of early reform. By the same token this exposé of the money power behind Christmas will not injure our own interests—for a long time to come THE CHRISTMAS BOOK should hold its own in the market for Seasonable Gifts.

Haters of Christmas

BY JAMES LAVER

O MOST PEOPLE in the modern world it seems incredible that anyone should ever have *hated* Christmas. It is true, of course, that, as we grow older, Christmas loses something of its magic; it no longer seems as wonderful as it used to do when we were young. And if we have no children through whom we can experience its delights anew, then we may perhaps begin to wonder if the pleasures of receiving presents, or even Christmas cards, is not perhaps outweighed by the trouble and boredom of sending them out. To be quite honest, I was rather glad myself when the war put an end to the Christmas card habit. I had got up to two or three hundred, and the mere addressing of the envelopes had become something of a burden. Some people dread the approach of Christmas because they can't trust themselves not to be greedy and every Boxing Day, in spite of all their good resolutions, find themselves suffering from acute indigestion.

But from all this to *hating* Christmas is a long cry, and yet history shows us that there have been people who regarded Christmas with a quite religious detestation—and I am using the word religious in its literal sense. I suppose I shall be accused of paradox if I say that the Early Christians hated Christmas; and yet even the most orthodox of reference books are compelled to admit that some such statement comes very much nearer to the truth than the opposite.

Perhaps one should qualify this by saying that the very Early Christians did not hate Christmas for the very good reason that they had no notion of any such festival. Unimpeachable authorities all agree that, fantastic as it seems, Christmas was *not* among the early festivals of the Church. There seems to have been no celebration of Christ's birth, as such, for the first two hundred years of the Christian era!

The first evidence of such a celebration comes from Egypt about the year A.D. 200, but it did not take place on December 25th but on May 20th. Others held that Christ's birth had happened on April 19th or 20th. Different views were maintained in different places, in fact 'there is no month in the year to which respectable authorities have not assigned Christ's birth'. The only thing that almost all seem to have been agreed about was that it was on a Wednesday!

However, there *was* a festival kept throughout the Roman world on December 25th. It was the festival of the Winter Solstice, the Feast of the Invincible Sun, who having descended to the lowest point of the horizon begins to rise again and so is, as it were, reborn. The Church in its wisdom, saw that here was an admirable opportunity to take over what was good in a pagan festival. A new meaning could be read into the old ceremonies and what had merely been the rebirth of the physical sun became the birth of the Sun of Righteousness. The mere saviour of the crops was transmuted and transformed into the Saviour of the World.

I do not know why anyone should object to this process. It seems to me to be full of meaning: the wise and kindly thought of some great religious genius who realised that the only way to rise at all was to ' rise on stepping stones of our dead selves to higher things '. But it did not happen without protest and there was quite a struggle before it could be brought about. The Church of Jerusalem resisted what it regarded as an innovation for a whole generation after the period when Christmas had got itself established at Rome.

Once it had got itself established it acted like a magnet and attracted towards itself all the charming motives which could in anyway be related to it. The Romans, the Ancient Romans, that is, had given one another presents at the Winter Solstice. It was a natural expression of the joy which all normal human beings must feel in the renewal of their hope. So we give presents at Christmas-time today, conscious that they will be repaid, if not by our friends, then by bounteous Nature and by the Giver of all. Perhaps that is putting it on too commercial a basis. Let us say rather that we give as an expression of gratitude for all we have ourselves received. The cynic may call this foolish but we can hardly call it contemptible.

What of the other ' properties ' of Christmas? What of the yule-log, what of the Christmas tree whose starry candles have delighted so many generations of children? The yule-log is the Old Year which, as it is consumed gives warmth to the new. This is a wonderful idea and I care little whether it is a ' pagan ' notion or not. It is a true symbol of a miracle that really happens, the miracle of the renewal of life. And the Christmas tree enshrines an even deeper and more splendid thought, for it is nothing but the Tree of the Universe and the candles on its branches are stars. But it took a long time to reach this country. One would like to think that our mediaeval ancestors had a Christmas tree in the baronial hall; one would like to think that Shakespeare, as a child, had gazed upon one in wonder. But the evidence is against us. It seems fairly certain that the Christmas tree was introduced into England by the Prince Consort in 1840.

We have had mistletoe for very much longer. We got it from the Druids, but those rather frightening people were certainly not in the habit of kissing under it. No one seems to know when *that* delightful custom came in. Anyway, Christmas tree or no Christmas tree, the Middle Ages in *Merry* England had no lack of feasting and frolic at Christmas, and it was not until the Age of the Puritans that anybody seems to have found very much to grumble at.

Now the Puritans had some admirable qualities, but they didn't hold with jollity of any kind. (They are not quite extinct today but their inhibitions clothe themselves in the jargon of economics rather than in the language of piety.) They disliked May Day revels, and all games, even games of skill; they disliked painting and poetry and music, and anything but ' utility ' clothes; they decried anything that might conceivably be called a recreation. But most of all they hated, they abominated Christmas.

Christmas was made illegal by Act of Parliament in the year 1644, that is, as soon as the Puritans had won their first successes against King Charles. They forbade shops to close on that day, and provided penalties for anyone who should be so hardy as to make, or eat, a plum pudding. The Puritans loved restrictions of every kind, but Englishmen in the seventeenth century were not so patient and long-suffering as they have since become. There were revolts all over the country —at Canterbury blood was shed. The Men of Kent were willing to fight to defend the right to eat plum pudding, and I wish I could record that they had been successful.

The Puritans were, for the moment, too strong for these admirable lovers of Liberty—I would that their names had been preserved—and Parliament set about the task of preventing such outbreaks in the future by bringing in new restrictions. On Christmas Eve 1652 the House of Commons (as we learn from a little pioneer newspaper with the charming name of *The Flying Eagle*) was ' presented with a terrible remonstrance against Christmas Day, grounded upon divine Scriptures . . . in which Christmas is called Anti-Christ's masse, and those Massemongers and Papists who observe it. In consequence of which Parliament spent some time in consultation about the abolition of Christmas Day, passed orders to that effect, and resolved to sit on the following day, which was commonly called Christmas Day.'

However, the efforts of Parliament to repress human nature do not seem to have been too successful, for, four years later a Member felt impelled to rise and say: ' I hope we shall all witness against this celebration, otherwise it will be set abroad that these superstitious days have their favourites in the House'!

In the same year one Hezekiah Wood called Christmas ' a day of drunkness and wantoness on which men serve the devil so devoutly at that time that they cannot cease from his worship, no more than he or they can cease from sin all the year after '.

However, Hezekiah Wood and his like had only another four years to try to abolish Christmas, for the Restoration brought in Christmas again, with King Charles himself seemingly determined to be the Lord of the Revels. Perhaps this is one of the reasons why Charles II, with all his faults, still has a place in our hearts.

After that Happy Restoration of Plum Pudding, the enemies of Christmas were silent for a space, and, when they reappeared again they had no religious or moral reasons on which to base their protests. For, by the middle of the nineteenth century, Christmas had shed whatever elements of the orgy and the primitive festival it had once possessed. It had become an eminently respectable institution. So the Scrooges of Dickens' day—for we have come to Scrooge at last—had nothing but sheer selfishness to fall back upon. When they were honest they had to confess that what they really objected to was the spectacle of people enjoying themselves.

' If I could work my will,' said Scrooge, ' every idiot who goes about with " Merry Christmas " on his lips, should be boiled in his own pudding, and buried with a stake of holly through his heart.'

Well, even Scrooge was converted at last, if not altogether in the world of reality, at least in the happier world which Dickens created out of the generosity of his own imagination. And Dickens pleaded with so much eloquence that now whatever Scrooges survive into our own day have to pretend to like Christmas whether they do or not.

So we have our Christmas, with its red berries and its white, albeit at an outrageous price; and its puddings, even if they have not so many plums in them as they once had, and the brandy which used to flame about their base is sadly lacking; and its turkey, even if it is only a chicken; and its Christmas tree even if it *is* less thickly hung with toys. Through many adversities and despite the hatred of the Puritans of all ages, Christmas has survived into our day; and may the time be far off when all its charming ceremonies and hoary legends are heard of no more.

The
Christmas Short-Story

BY MARGHANITA LASKI

'HE ENGLISH,' once said an interested foreigner, 'were created two drinks below par.' The English themselves are prone to believe that the foreigners were created gallons more than two drinks above it, but that's beside the point I'm really leading up to, which is an investigation of one of the methods by which the Island Race tries to achieve the presumably desirable state of Par.

Some, of course, have a shot at it all the year round by imbibing the requisite two drinks as often as possible. But—quite apart from current shortages—that isn't the English way. The Island Race is perfectly content, not to say proud, to spend most of the year in the frame of mind that it itself describes as British Phlegm, and then pep itself up to Par on a few suitable occasions such as Bank Holidays, Cup Finals, Ends of Wars and, of course, Christmas.

Now man being a creature of custom, it is extremely likely by now that the pepping up on each of these occasions could take place quite naturally; but not enough people are content to leave the process to nature. Far from it. And at Christmas more than at any other time, the pepping up of the nation has become a national industry. From approximately the twenty-seventh of December of each year, half the population starts thinking about the money it's going to induce the other half—and ultimately, by a process of auto-intoxication, itself—to spend before the next Christmas has been and gone. And no one starts in earlier than the Christmas short-story writer who, sometime before Midsummer Day, has got to have his Christmas short story thought of, neatly typed up, and, of course, accepted.

Goodness knows, I don't, how many magazines with short stories in them are published each Christmas. Goodness knows how many short-story-writers are engaged in filling them. But when you consider that each of these magazines is going to have from one to three-plus short-stories in its December issue, all designed to foster the Spirit of Christmas in all their readers, you begin to get some idea of the dimensions of this particular branch of the Christmas industry.

Mind you, the work isn't really arduous. There are only about seven themes for Christmas short-stories and they are all sure-fire hits. Rehash, rewrite, reshape as you will, these stories remain basically the same, each one absolutely guaranteed to wring a tear from a normally maudlin eye.

Let us proceed to our examination:

The first story nearly always has some rather moving title taken from a familiar Christmas quotation like *No Room At The Inn*, is illustrated with lush colour, and is principally directed at what I might call a Matron-Public. It is about a humble pregnant woman who, for some rather complicated reason, is on the march. It is Christmas Eve. The humble pregnant woman is near her time and has nowhere to rest her head. But stay—what is this building before her?

So far, so conventional, but here the individual writer's ingenuity must manifest itself. The humble pregnant woman may end up, for instance, at a loveless wealthy mansion where husband and wife are at loggerheads and Unmindful of the Meaning of Things. Or she may arrive at another loveless rich mansion where a Little Child has died not so long ago. Or at yet another—England is known to be a land of country-houses—where a loveless old woman is lovelessly regretting her hardness to a turned-from-the-roof loved one these many years gone.

Do I need to go on? The humble pregnant woman has her infant in an adjoining barn, never never *never* managing to stumble quite so far as the loveless mansion itself. And the loveless rich inhabitants come and gaze at the infant and there is wonder in their eyes and they remember that it's Christmas Eve and all sorts of parallels suddenly strike them and, in short, they have one of those miraculous changes of heart that are so pathetically the pipe-dream of the mal-adjusted. And the reader mops the maudlin eye and says between sobs, ' I really mustn't forget little Mrs. Blenkinsop this year,' and another five bob is marked down to swell the volume of the Christmas trade.

Story number two is intended rather for modern up-to-date skittish magazines catering for, in department-store phraseology, maids rather than matrons. In this one Belinda (as a matter of fact she is usually called Carol nowadays, but I loathe the name) Belinda, I said, is alone. It is, of course, Christmas Eve. But Christmas Eve means nothing to Belinda for she has no one to share it with and so she says, very naturally, that she'd sooner be alone, that she's no use for all this slush and sentiment, that she just doesn't care. (Where is she alone, you ask? Well, usually in her little flatlet in Chelsea.)

You know and I know, though Belinda doesn't, that all this careless nonchalance is just a phony, and even the unsuspecting Belinda is usually wiping an uncomprehended tear from her eye with a corner of her floral apron when the young man who also hates Christmas appears on the scene. How to get him on is, of course, the measure of each writer's craft; personally, I rather like the version where he suddenly appears at the window and is mistaken for a gas inspector.

Quite a lot of this particular story is taken up with that peculiar form of semi-hostile badinage that passes for the preliminary stages of love-making among the Anglo-Saxons. The effect of all this is to make the reader feel pleasantly sophisticated in a rather Noel-Coward-New-Yorker sort of way, and only too ready, after Belinda and her young man have achieved apotheosis in an inept embrace and agreed to hang up some holly together, to say, ' Now I really must remember to buy some French perfume for Jennifer—poor dear, she *does* need it ', and another two guineas has swollen the Christmas trade.

The third story we have to examine can be provisionally entitled ' And a Little Child——' and is beamed towards the spinster who hasn't married, in contra-distinction to the last which is meant for the one who intends to. This story is a real orgy of tears. There are two principal characters, one the little lost lonely pathetic abused unhappy child and the other the lonely unhappy unwanted spinster, very often a school-mistress who doesn't feel that she's quite the success she might be with the Upper Fifth—ah, *there's* a human situation for you. By the time these two have been through all the vicissitudes that can be induced by hunger, cold, poverty, snubs and what have you, and Two Lonely Hearts have come Together, you are perfectly conditioned to murmur, ' Poor old Miss Timms—I'm sure she'd be glad of a nice warm scarf '.

The fourth story is the historico-reverent one that tells the story of the birth at Bethlehem as seen by a Magi or a shepherd or even a camel. It is usually illustrated by wood-engravings.

The fifth story is the Scrooge story.

The sixth story depends on the international situation and is therefore only occasional. It is the story of the Christmas Spirit rearing its head amidst the Brutality of Battle and often centres round a child or a dog.

The last story is a comparatively new one and comes from across the Atlantic. The heroine is at the age that Longfellow envisaged as *Standing with reluctant feet Where the brook and river meet*, but is nowadays, I understand, more tersely described as a bobby-soxer. This unpleasant adolescent, a small-town girl, has an older sister whom, with an almost pathological absence of tact, she inevitably humiliates before her young man. She has a kid brother who is, judging from the way she treats him, likely to suffer from a lifelong inferiority complex if not worse. Indeed, she is so horrible that I can hardly bear to reveal to you that at Christmas time her downtrodden family regard her with something like awe—or is it, maybe, relief—when she puts on her first high-heeled shoes to go out with her first beau. I may add that when accepting this story, editors usually change Westchester County to Surrey and Fifth Avenue to Bond Street, thus unreasonably giving their readers the impression that English social life is like that. And then, presumably, the reader murmurs, ' Yes, it *is* time that I bought young Jemima her first lipstick ', although she'd probably be wiser to give her an acne ointment.

Now this last story is, in a very interesting way, different from the six that preceded it; it need not be used only at Christmas but can, with very slight adaptations, be sold all the year round. I imagine that, for some fascinating sociological reason, this particular story has such a grip on the American public that they can never bear to be without it.

On this side of the Atlantic, the situation is quite other. We make a very clear distinction between *Christmas* and what I might call *secular* short-story writing. The Christmas story is an art all its own and none of the secular favourites ever dress up in some new disguise and feign to represent it. Not that story of Mistress Barbara Whosit and the dashing pirate who looks like James Mason. Not that story of the salmon, dogfish, eagle, okapi, whose author always knows its—can one say *Christian*—name and every dark deep earthly impulse that stirs beneath its feathers, scales or hide. Not that story of love coming to the professional woman who used, in my childhood, to be a nurse, in my adolescence a woman doctor, and is now, in my maturity, a literary-agent. And most certainly not that story about the husband who is being unfaithful to his wife, and who always used to be got back by a facial and a new hat, but is increasingly inclined to stay with the floosie to whom our sympathies now tend to be directed.

I wouldn't want you to think I was cynical. I would ask you to remember that I am writing this in March when you can hardly pretend that the Christmas spirit is really under way. You will be reading it in December—that's to say, if production goes according to schedule—with a warm glow in your heart and a general feeling of benevolence all around you. And by that time, I'll be so much infected with the auto-intoxication of the season, that I'll be feeling the same way too.

So picture us, you and I, sitting by our respective fires, thumbing the Christmas magazines and reading just these stories with every evidence of eager anticipation and enjoyment. And when we've finished the last story, we will close the magazine and say, with a benevolent glow, ' Now this year we really mustn't forget young Jemima and Poor Old Miss Timms and Jennifer and Little Miss Blenkinsop and Uncle Tom Cobley and All '. And never mind about the Christmas Trade, it's the benevolent glow that counts. Friends, for this brief season and thanks, in some measure to the Christmas short-story writer, we are up to Par.

OLD
and
NEW

CHRISTMAS in the pictorial tradition has come to mean snow and ice no less than plum pudding (round like a football), gift-decked Christmas trees and lantern-lit carol singers. This collection of pictorial variations on the traditional themes originally set out to show by means of photographs of the nineteen-forties, side by side with engravings of the eighteen-forties, the *difference* between the accepted view of Yuletide today and yesterday—but the final result has achieved the opposite effect. We have unwittingly evolved a demonstration of how obstinately the old tradition clings. *Plus ça change*, in fact.

CHRISTMAS WAITS IN THE COUNTRY (Birkett Foster)

'BRIGHTLY SHONE THE MOON THAT NIGHT' (Sitensky, Prague)

'NO ENEMY BUT WINTER AND ROUGH WEATHER' (Birkett Foster)

A COTTAGE IN THE SOUTH OF BOHEMIA (Sitensky, Prague)

ICE ON THE POND AT HAMPSTEAD HEATH (Suschitzky)

'THE SKATING SEASON ON THE SERPENTINE'

A SNOW MANTLE IN HAMPSTEAD CHURCHYARD (Bill Brandt)

CHRISTMAS MORNING: GOING TO CHURCH

SNOW IN BLOOM (Sitensky)

THE HOLLY CART (Birkett Foster)

FARMYARD IN THE SNOW (Birkett Foster)

CHRISTMAS TREE COUNTRY (Sitensky)

'MR. WEBB'S NEW PANTOMIME CHARACTERS'

A POSSIBLE ASPIRANT FOR MR. MILLS (George Parmiter)

MAGIC MORNING (Shaw Wildman)

THE FIRST ENGLISH CHRISTMAS TREE—AT WINDSOR

Courtesy Harper's Bazaar

THE PARTY BREAKS UP (Maurice Tabard)

THE SNOW MAN (Suschitzky)

SNOW SWEEPERS (Birkett Foster)

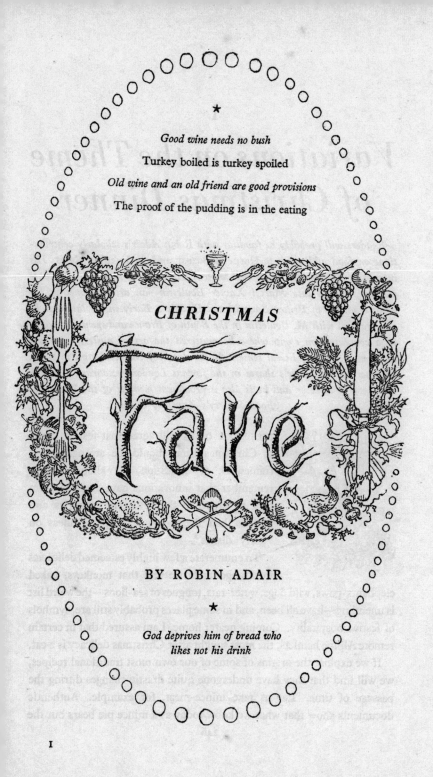

Good wine needs no bush

Turkey boiled is turkey spoiled

Old wine and an old friend are good provisions

The proof of the pudding is in the eating

CHRISTMAS

Fare

BY ROBIN ADAIR

God deprives him of bread who
likes not his drink

1

Variations on the Theme of Christmas Dinner

Readers will probably be familiar with Robin Adair's scholarly contributions on food and drink to Harper's Bazaar *and the* Evening News. *His interesting background is less well known. He was, for some years, private secretary to the late Marcel Xavier Boulestin—an arch-gourmet in the great tradition of Brillat-Savarin and Escoffier. Early in the late war he was trapped with M. Boulestin in the South of France and spent four years in a concentration camp where he mastered the art of austerity cooking in its most brutally literal sense. At the death of M. Boulestin, in 1943, he inherited the latter's shares in the famous London restaurant of which he is now a director and he is also a prominent member of the Wine and Food Society's Advisory Council.*

 HILE MOST OF US will agree that festive meals at Christmas time should be arranged on a framework of Tradition, we should always remember that innovations have crept in from time to time and that different countries and periods had their own very special ideas on 'party dishes'.

To enumerate a few highly esteemed delicacies in strange lands we find that monkeys, baked elephants' paws, wild dogs, water-rats, tongues of sea-lions—the weird list is unending—have all been, and in some places probably still are, symbols of festive hospitality. Coming nearer home, I am assured that in certain remote Alpine hamlets, the most sought after Christmas delicacy is a cat.

If we explore the origins of some of our own most traditional recipes, we will find that they have undergone quite drastic changes during the passage of time. Let us take mince-meat, for example. Authentic documents show that what we know today as a mince pie bears but the

246

slightest resemblance to the 'Minced Pyes' of seventeenth-century England: 'My Lady of Portland told me that she finds Neats tongues to be the best flesh for pies' . . . then follows a list of other ingredients including 'Raisins of the Sun and Candid Orange Peel' . . . But 'My Lady Lasson holdeth the most savoury mince pyes to be of veal and mutton in equal parts'. So it is with Christmas pudding which has not only changed out of all recognition but is not the exclusively English speciality we so often presume it to be; which brings me to a French Christmas meal I can still remember as one of the most perfect I have ever met.

It was the *réveillon* supper, after midnight mass on Christmas Eve, in the house of typically French people and there was no question of imitating English fashions, as this menu will prove:

Consommé en Tasse
Saucisses aux Huitres
Dinde Truffée
Salade Demi-Deuil
Pouding de Noël

There was nothing extraordinary about the *consommé* excepting its perfection. But the oysters—great succulent green ones from Marennes, were served not only with brown bread and butter but with separate plates of piping-hot, crisp fried sausages; a most exquisite, subtle contrast, slightly surprising till one remembered our own 'Angels on Horseback'. The difficulty was in juggling with only two hands to be able to eat an oyster, take a piece of hot sausage at the same time as a bite of bread, while trying to drink the exquisite dry white Burgundy which accompanied the lot.

The turkey had been treated in the grand manner. Twenty-four hours before cooking it, the whole of the outside had been truffled; that is, slices of truffle had been inserted under the skin with a sharp pointed knife and the bird stuffed with its *farce* of sausage meat, chestnuts and chopped truffle. It was then trussed and left in a cool larder to be impregnated with the incomparable *truffe* flavour.

No potatoes were served, only those in the salad of which they and truffle, both cut *en julienne* (match-like strips) were the ingredients.

When the pudding came, our hostess explained that she was specially proud of it as the recipe was from a family recipe book started in the 1840's; the finishing touch was given on the table. The whole of the top was covered with sugar over which warm brandy was generously poured. Then a layer of butter was added, more brandy which was then set alight, the pudding being basted with the flaming spirit till the butter and sugar had melted and the flames had died out naturally. It was the very best Christmas pudding I have ever tasted.

To go back to the bird, it is a mistake to think that it must be a turkey. Many people infinitely prefer goose or even really fat ducklings; one of the most admirable Christmas dinners I have eaten had a delicious main dish of wild ducks which had been caught alive and kept until really fattened. They were plainly roasted and served with an elaborate sauce made with their own gravy—not thickened but with fat removed—to which were added Madeira and shredded oranges. Geese can be served in many ways: with red cabbage and chestnuts, braised with apples and cream or on a bed of hearts of tender white cabbages.

Another great mistake which is commonly made is to serve—at all times, but it is even more objectionable on festive occasions—a whole lot of unnecessary vegetables with the bird. When it is stuffed or cooked with some garnish such as I have just described, we do not want anything but some amusingly cooked potatoes: *rissolées*—small ones, browned whole in a saucepan in fat; or *parisiennes*—scooped out into little balls first par-boiled in boiling salted water, well dried and then browned in butter: either of these are just right and with the bird I would also serve a salad of some kind. The more elaborate the treatment of the bird, the simpler the salad should be, though a mixture of lettuce and orange is not only permissible but to be recommended as it takes off some of the richness.

And now I will give another simple menu, this time of my own:

Bouillon de Poisson
Turkey or Goose
Stuffing or garnishing
Pommes Rissolées
Salad
Christmas Pudding
Céleri en Surprise

The clear fish soup is an ideal beginning to what is bound to be a rather rich meal. It is simply made by tossing, in a mixture of oil and butter, a few vegetables cut up: leek, onion, carrot and a *bouquet* of thyme, parsley and bay-leaf. We add portions of any kind of fish cut up in pieces—say, cod and whiting; it need not be expensive fish—salt and pepper. Cook for a minute or two and add a pinch of curry powder and one of saffron. Stir over the fire for another minute or so then add boiling water, allowing a third more than you will require of soup, so that when it evaporates and reduces, you will have the right amount. Bring to the boil, reduce heat and just simmer for about thirty to forty minutes. Pass through a strainer, then through a fine muslin so that it is quite clear, and put in a clean saucepan to keep hot.

With this *bouillon* serve little round croûtons of bread, first fried golden brown then sprinkled with grated cheese and a pinch of saffron, after which you brown them quickly under the grill.

The *Céleri en Surprise* rounds off our meal crisply. We take good heads of celery and prepare them in the usual way, removing all outside leaves. Now make a mixture of butter (or margarine) and Roquefort or Danish blue cheese. Add pepper, a dash of Worcester sauce if it is liked and work well until you have a smooth paste. Now, without letting them break away from the head, open out the celery stalks so that you can spread inside with a flexible knife, the cheese mixture. Spread it as evenly as you can, press back the outer stalks and tie the stick with cotton. Put it in the refrigerator till wanted, remove the cotton and cut the stuffed celery into conveniently sized pieces.

2
Glasses, Large and Small

'RINK,' writes André Simon, ' is the law of life. To live, all must drink, man and beast, young and old, large and small.' He goes on to quote a verse of the Greek poet Anacreon, written 2,500 years ago:

> ' *Fill up the bowl, then, fill it high,*
> *Fill all the glasses there, and why*
> *Should every creature drink but I,*
> *Why, man of morals, tell me why?* '

What was sound philosophy then, as at all times of every year, might have been written specially for our present purpose and no one will deny that the quintessence of seasonable hospitality is a well-filled glass.

By well-filled I do not only mean as to quantity—anybody can pour a nondescript liquid from a bottle; no, I am more concerned with the choice and the quality since we are the discriminating, we are the *élite*, and whether it is a cocktail, a cup, or a punch that we have bidden our guests to drink with us, that drink is as near to perfection as our resources will permit. . . .

Let us start with cocktails and see what we can do in spite of restrictions.

For large parties, there should be two cocktails: a strong, very dry one (Dry Martini) and a milder, not so dry concoction perhaps of our own invention; the *specialité de la maison* so to speak—I will give suggestions further on.

When it is a question of the cocktail before a dinner-party our choice should be guided by the wines we are going to serve. The finer the wines the simpler, 'cleaner' the cocktail and I think the best mixture on such occasions is of gin and fresh fruit juice—orange, tangerine or grapefruit. In fact the cocktail should be no more than the conventional gesture which civilisation demands and pass almost unnoticed in the feelings of anticipation of the great things to come.

But if we can serve only one wine, not of course bad, but of no outstanding merit, then the cocktail must be given more importance and be of the speciality type. It is the wine then which will be no more than a pleasant drink accompanying good food. Before going on to some practical formulae and suggestions, there are one or two points about cocktail mixing the importance of which cannot be over-rated.

First of all, insist on all cocktails being properly iced and not allowed to get tepid. Avoid watery ones—nothing is more nauseating than a tepid, watery liquid. Dry Martinis and the other severely simple mixtures should be made freshly, as and when needed. The more elaborate concoctions can be made up in advance but not iced until the last minute.

Try and get the best possible ingredients; if you are at all doubtful about any of them—and this applies specially to the Vermouths—don't risk it, try and think of something else.

Dry Martini: The best proportion is two-thirds gin to one third *French* Vermouth; some people are content with half and half. Add ice and shake and, when poured out, squeeze over and drop into each glass, a small piece of lemon peel. When good Vermouth is not available it is better to substitute good dry Sherry. It won't be a Dry Martini but it will be an excellent cocktail.

Suggestions for inventions—One: gin, whisky and dry sherry in equal proportions with half a teaspoonful of bottled grapefruit juice for each person. Shake with ice and serve in glasses in which are small olives.

Two: Half whisky, half gin and a teaspoonful per person of lemon-barley water. A few drops of orange bitters.

Three: Half rum, one quarter Dubonnet or Byrrh, one quarter gin. Add a good dash of orange juice and plenty of ice.

Four: Two-thirds rum, one third fresh lemon juice, strained. For each person add half a teaspoonful of the jelly part of plum jam. Ice and shake vigorously to break up the jelly. This is a most subtle and intriguing mixture.

For these four cocktails—my own 'discoveries'—you must find amusing names to suit the occasion.

Now we come to the question of long drinks: cups and punches which are *par excellence* the drinks for Christmas entertainments.

For cups, I always use the same basis into which I pour the wine—either white or red—later, only splashing in a little soda water at the last minute. At very large parties it is rather a good plan to make both white and red wine cups and champagne or cyder can, of course, be treated in the same way. For smaller, intimate and informal parties a pink cup is always a success and can be easily made by mixing white and red wine, since there appears to be but little *Vin Rosé* yet available.

Cup Basis: Put in large jugs or bowls, some orange and lemon slices, together with the rinds of one of each. Other fruits may be added; grapes, a peach, cherries, raspberries, currants, all of these latter bottled, needless to say. But in any case they are not essential. Mint *should* be put in and cucumber rind, but in these days we may have to content ourselves with bottled fruit juices only. Now put in some sugar, not too much at first—we can always add more later if necessary—the final amount being entirely a question of taste. Over all this we pour whatever spirits we have available and any of the usual ones will do: whisky, gin, rum or brandy and, whenever it can be managed, a very little sweet liqueur as well. Stir all this up, cover the bowl or jug with a clean cloth and let it stand for four or five hours. Have the wine thoroughly well iced meanwhile and, about one hour before serving, pour it in. Taste to see if the cup is sufficiently sweet and well-flavoured and only at the very last moment splash in just sufficient soda water to give a little life and sparkle—who was it who wrote ' Heaven sent us soda water as a torment for our crimes '?

Well, it is now getting late. We have been through all the phases of the party and soon will come the apotheosis, the supreme moment of the *Punch.* There is endless scope for the adventurous. . . .

Old-fashioned Mulled Wine: A simple affair of heating in a saucepan some ordinary red wine and cinnamon and sugar to taste. Let it come nearly, but not quite, to the boil and pour it into each glass containing a slice of lemon.

Cyder Punch: A hilarious affair of cyder in a saucepan with oranges—

say one orange for from four to six people—stuck with half a dozen cloves; sugar or not according to taste. Bring to the boil, simmer for five minutes or so and put in a good 'tot' of gin per person.

Apple Punch: For every couple of guests, put in a saucepan a freshly baked apple. Sprinkle with sugar and pour in just enough boiling water to dissolve the sugar, stirring. Stir in a good glass of brandy or rum per person and add sufficient boiling water to make up the requisite of glasses.

Punch Flambé: Put into a metal punch bowl a slice each of orange and lemon per person. Add sugar, grated nutmeg and cinnamon (also cloves, if liked) and then put in a mixture of rum and brandy which you set alight. Stir with a ladle till the flames die and dilute with boiling water.

Tea Punch: A delicious drink is made with freshly brewed tea poured through a strainer into the punch bowl over a basis made like the one for the *flambé* punch—only without burning it.

After a good glass of any of these drinks we should be in excellent mood to tackle whatever the grim grey dawn has in store for us.

253

3

Party Sweets

F WE THINK seriously about the Englishman in his rigid observance of Christmas rites, we must admit that he sets a fine example, for there is more in this than merely childish excitement or an excuse for frivolity at all costs. No, he is an example of determination to protect ancient customs in the teeth of every possible obstacle and he is more than nobly supported by his wife in this admirable attitude. Continuing to add my own contributions to the good cause, let me proffer some suggestions for party sweets—starting with a few words about:

Pastry I: A simplified recipe for *Short Pastry* which would make a good tart for six people or small ones for eight. Sieve eight ounces of flour into a mixing bowl, add a teaspoonful of baking powder and a pinch of salt. Have ready-mixed two ounces of lard and two of margarine or butter, breaking it up into little pieces; these are rubbed into the flour. Now add, little by little, about half a tumbler of cold water working to a smooth dough which you turn out on to a floured board. Roll out lightly until you have a square or round of pastry slightly larger than your tart tin. Grease the tin and line with pastry. Before baking, paint all over with a little milk and dust with castor sugar. Cook for about a quarter of an hour.

Pastry II, puff: The lightness and 'puff' is achieved by getting as much cold air as possible into the paste before it goes into a hot oven. We do this by rolling and folding several times in as cool a place as possible. In this case, for eight ounces of flour we require six of fat, half lard and half margarine or butter. Having sieved the flour, added salt and baking powder, we rub in the fat—also divided up into small pieces. Make a hole in the middle and start adding the cold water, little by little till we have our smooth dough. Dust the pastry board and rolling pin with flour and roll out the dough, very lightly, to a long strip. Fold this in three and roll out again, repeating this process three times. If you can start early, leave an interval of ten minutes or so between each rolling, keeping the dough in a very cool place during the intervals. When ready to bake, roll out for the last time and cut into whatever shape and size are required. Bake in greased tin or tins for about fifteen minutes in a hot oven.

Fillings : All sorts of fillings can be used: bottled or fresh fruit—when the fruit is of a dry kind such as apple slices, a layer of jam first. Apple slices are also improved if raisins, cinnamon and brown sugar are added. A well-flavoured thick custard or a chocolate or toffee custard are good and a tart with a custard basis with fruit on top is perfect. An amusing idea for children's parties is to add spices—cinnamon, nutmeg, mixed spice—to the dough before rolling and cut it into primitive figures of people and animals. Buttons and eyes can be made of currants and peel.

Ices : Here are two basic recipes which can be carried out even in restricted periods, since most of us can manage to scrape up an egg or two for these special occasions.

First of all you want a tin of evaporated milk which you stand—unopened—in a pan of boiling water. Let the water boil for two or three minutes, cool the tin and keep it in the refrigerator overnight. Open the tin and take a tablespoonful of the milk in which you dissolve a teaspoonful of gelatine. Whip up the rest, adding the dissolved gelatine until it is quite frothy and incorporate this with the white of two eggs, also whipped. Fold in two tablespoonfuls of icing sugar and whatever flavouring you are using: coffee, chocolate, chopped nuts, fruit syrup, candied peel, etc. Turn the mixture into the ice cube trays of the refrigerator and freeze quickly.

The second basic ice is even simpler for present conditions: you take half a tin of unsweetened milk and the same quantity of cold water, mixing the two. Use a very little of this liquid to mix half an ounce of cornflour to a smooth paste. Boil the rest and pour it over the cornflour blend. Add four ounces of sugar and whatever flavouring you are using and, when this is done, pour into the ice cube trays and freeze. As the mixture starts freezing, scrape it away from the sides of the tray and work it in with the rest; repeat this two or three times before finally freezing. (*Note :* When a vanilla flavouring is required for this method,

255

the best way is to boil a vanilla pod with the milk. These pods can be washed, dried and left to be used five or six times.

Mousses : All sorts of mousses can be easily made by following the recipe for the first ice given above. It is simply a question of treating the tin of evaporated milk to the boiling process, afterwards making it icy cold before whipping and mixing the gelatine. This cream is then ready to be treated and flavoured with whatever you have decided upon and put away in a mould or a soufflé dish to be made cold, but not frozen, on a shelf of the refrigerator.

Jellies : A particularly good method of treating jelly crystals is to melt the crystals in the smallest possible quantity of boiling water, and add a good extra flavouring of rum. The right quantity of liquid is then made up with *cold* milk and the whole thing put away, after beating it all up together, in the coldest possible part of the refrigerator. The result is a very subtle tasting mousse-jelly with an intriguing flecked appearance. Turn out of a pretty mould and top with a little well-sweetened and flavoured whipped cream.

A Christmas Cake: It may be difficult to achieve this year, but not impossible and so the recipe which follows can be considered as a link between the old world and the new. But it is also the recipe for a really good cake.

Put into an empty paper bag one pound of flour and a heaped teaspoonful of baking powder, shaking the bag to mix well; then sieve the flour. Have a warm bowl into which you put half a pound of butter or margarine and half a pound of castor sugar and stand the bowl sufficiently near some heat to enable the contents to become soft without danger of melting to oil. Now prepare a mixture of fruits—about a pound and a half altogether of raisins, currants, sultanas, sweet almonds or just seedless raisins if the others are not available; all these de-pipped and stalked, the almonds blanched, peeled and chopped—and mix them with the flour. Beat, with the hand, its warmth being essential, the butter and sugar, and add four eggs, one at a time, beating each one in separately: if powdered eggs are used—diluted, of course, with water—add them in four movements, beating each quarter in separately. To this mixture, beat in the flour and fruits and moisten with a little milk to the usual consistency for a cake batter. Put into a well-greased tin and bake for about three hours in a moderate oven.

The NEW CHRISTMAS DINNER SONG.

CHRISTMAS time is now approaching
      Doodah, doodah,
I on your time must be encroaching,
      Oh, doodah, doodahda.
All the children, James and Nelly,
      Doodah, doodah,
With goose & pudding will fill their bellies
      O my! O my, O!

    They are going to eat all night,
      Dance and blow your clay;
    Then blow out your tripes with goose
      so nice,
    For you know its Christmas day.

This goose is to be a nummer,
When the insides out its a twelve stunner,
From the head to the tail it will measure
    a mile, sir,
Dressed up & cooked in regular style, sir

Ten thousand ladies of it will dine, sir,
And work it down with a hogshead of wine
    sir,
With crinolines so fat and plump,
With feathers in their hats from the
    goose's rump.

Six tons of suet, chopped quite fine,
Cod liver oil and old port wine;
Ten sacks of flour—enough for a meal,
A hogshead of sugar and a ton of peel.

They're going to boil it on board the
    Eastern,
That half the world will have a feast, man,
The greens and potatoes will be boiled, I
    declare,
In the net bags that holds up the ladies
    hair.

After dinner its all the go, sir,
To kiss girls under the miseltoe, sir,
Fo the dance, girls take their places,
Some turn jealous and get scratched faces.

Little, big, fat, and tall and thin,
Can't kisss them for their crinolines.
Cut away boys at half-past six,
Smash the hoops—go at it like bricks.

Up the sides and down the middle,
The fiddler's drunk and so is the fiddle;
They have drank so much their throats
    are roasting,
Run for the doctor the cooks are bursting.

They have eat all the goose and like an
    old good'un,
They swore they'd polish the rest of the
    pudding;
Tom has eat twelve pounds and would
    like a score,
He's crying because he can't eat any more

Its six o'clock, and the cocks give warning,
They all pig together and sleep until morn-
    ing;
Lets hope you'll all be happy and gay,
And be just like this on christmas day.

May you get drunk at night,
And eat goose and pudding all day;
If your appetite's right, feed really you
    must,
For you know its chrismas day.

TAYLOR, Printer, 92 & 93, Brick-lane,
    Spitalfieles.

CHRISTMAS BROADSHEET SOLD IN THE STREETS ABOUT A HUNDRED AND FIFTY YEARS AGO

257

APPENDIX

1. ANSWERS TO QUIZ ON PAGES 190–193

SWIFT WORK. Moll is a beauty, has an acute eye. No lass so fine is, Molly divine is. O my dear mistress, I'm in a distress. Can't you discover me as a lover?

1ST DOCTOR: Is his honour sick? Pray let us feel his pulse. It does beat very slow today.

2ND DOCTOR: No no, 'tis as quick as I ever felt. You may try it. Indeed it is as fast as an alarum, or a fire bell at night.

3RD DOCTOR: It is very high!

4TH DOCTOR: Not to contradict you, in my judgement it is very low today. It is a sort o' malady, some call it.

SPEAKING OF THAT. Try reading the sentence: The gentleman said, in speaking of the word 'that', that that 'that' that that lady parsed was not that 'that' that that gentleman had asked her to analyse.

KNOW ANYTHING? 1. *a.* Appleby. *b.* Oakham. *c.* Bodmin. *d.* Lewes. 2. *a.* Bangkok. *b.* Mexico City. *c.* Pretoria. *d.* Managua. 3. *a.* Thailand is the official name for Siam, which lies between Burma and China. *b.* Central America. *c.* French West Africa. *d.* Norfolk. 4. Probably quite a number of people, but they were all misquoting from the following sources: *a.* Shakespeare (To gild refined gold, to paint the lily). *b.* Pope (A little learning is a dangerous thing). *c.* Shakespeare (Lay on, Macduff). *d.* James Thomson (Rule Britannia! Britannia, rule the waves).

5. *a.* Bookseller. *b.* Collector of books. *c.* Lover of books. *d.* Collector of bindings (Bookbinder). 6. *a.* York. *b.* Istanbul (Constantinople is *not* the modern name). *c.* Brighton. *d.* St. Albans.

WILBERFORCE'S PUZZLE. Chest — eyelids — kneecaps — ear drums — veins — hand, foot, nail — arms — nails — soles — muscles — palms — apples — heart (hart) — hairs (hares) — temples — pupils — insteps — tendons (ten Dons) — lashes — calves — nose.

THE LAST WORD. 1. Keats. 2. Anne Boleyn (holding her neck). 3. Sir Walter Raleigh. 4. Queen Elizabeth. 5. Cromwell. 6. William Pitt. 7. Goethe. 8. Charles II.

LETTER PERFECT? 1. The letter L. 2. B, R, and Y. 3. Because without it they cannot have birthdays or Christmas. 4. It is the capital of England. 5. Glass—lass—ass. 6. A, because it makes her hear. 7. *Facetiously* and *abstemiously*.

LOCAL COLOUR. *a.* Lemster. *b.* Muell. *c.* Wumundham. *d.* Wyndham. *e.* Launston. *f.* Casehorton. *g.* Possit. *h.* Cicester. *i.* Kircuebry. *j.* Dee-ell. *k.* Strawn. *l.* Coppersmith.

CHESTNUTS. 1. Because the higher the fewer. 2. Because there's a B in both. 3. His father's name was Bodger. 4. Eleven. 5. A difference of opinion. 6. Because he makes a little go a long way. 7. Nothing. 8. A cat looking in a window. 9. Short. 10. When it's hard rode. 11. Both are over-officious. 12. The horse dealer was cheating; mules cannot reproduce.

CHARADES. Ant-elope. Man-age.

NO JIGGERY-POKERY. A few to be going on with: handy-pandy, higgledy-piggledy, hodge-podge, hotch-potch, hoity-toity, helter-skelter, hanky-panky, harum-scarum, hugger-mugger hum-drum, hurdy-gurdy, hurly-burly, hurry-scurry, kicksie-wicksie, mumbo-jumbo, niminy-piminy, pell-mell, pow-wow, ran-dan.

The circle may be drawn with a piece of chalk round the person's body.

ASK ME ANOTHER. 1. Railway guard. The missing word is card, Christmas card. 2. First visitor at a house after midnight on New Year's Eve. A custom still popular in Scotland. 3. From holy bush, because the berries ripen about Christmas. 4. Because it was written for performance on Twelfth Night, 6th January, 1602. 5. In England from the seventh to the thirteenth century. 6. In 1752 in England. From the fourteenth century until then, New Year's Day was on March 25th.

2. ANSWERS TO QUIZ ON PAGE 199

1. As the Nativity of Christ, not until the fourth or fifth century A.D., though a pagan midwinter festival has existed since early primitive times.

2. In 1644, by Act of Parliament repealed at the Restoration.

3. (i) This is a relic of an earlier festival than Christmas, when, round about the shortest day of the year, lights or bonfires were kindled to invoke the sun's return.

(ii) Continuance of the tradition of singing Christmas hymns or carols begun by wandering minstrels who 'waited' the pleasure of the lord of the manor. Later, the watchmen who called the time and the weather took on the job and, when policemen were introduced in 1820, it fell to private individuals to carry on.

(iii) Mistletoe was the sacred tree of the Druids and various primitive peoples; kissing under the sacred tree is, therefore, a survival of an idolatrous custom and has nothing to do with Christmas.

4. (i) Russian. He is a corruption of St. Nicholas. Early Dutch settlers in America called him San Nicolaas and celebrated his feast on December 6th. Americans turned him into Santa Claus and attached him to Christmas. (ii) He was King of Bohemia (now Czechoslovakia). (iii) Italian.

5. (i) U.S.A. (ii) Poland. (iii) Yugoslavia (the Croats).

6. (i) January 6th. (ii) December 26th. (iii) December 31st.

7. (i) W. Somerset Maugham. (ii) Charles Dickens. (iii) George R. Sims.

8. (i) A Christmas game in which raisins are snatched from burning brandy. (ii) A white-petalled hellebore flowering at Christmas. Not a rose. (iii) Mulled wheat boiled in milk and mixed with spices, eaten at Christmas.

9. (i) From the custom of giving gifts or 'boxes' on the first weekday after Christmas. (ii) From the old English 'Waes hál' (be whole!), a

drinking toast. (iii) They were priests of ancient Persia or magicians (from Persian 'magus'). The term was applied to the wise men from the East.

10. (i) Custom borrowed from primitive tribes who held a fire festival at midwinter and burnt logs of wood.

(ii) Another pre-Christian survival. The boar was the animal form of the corn-spirit, and was sacrificed and decorated with evergreen garlands.

(iii) Turkey is merely an English substitute for the boar's head and the sausages (chains) represent the garlands which surrounded it.

11. (i) William the Conqueror, crowned on Christmas Day, 1066. (ii) Noel Coward, born December 16th, 1899. (iii) Princess Alexandra, daughter of the Duchess of Kent. Born December 25th, 1936.

12. (i) 'Peter Pan.' (ii) 'Where the Rainbow Ends.' (iii) 'The Blue Bird.'

13. (i) Tschaikowski (from the 'Nutcracker Suite.') (ii) Corelli. (iii) J. S. Bach.

14. (i) 'God rest you merry, Gentlemen.' (ii) 'We, three kings of Orient are.' (iii) 'Love and Joy come to you.'

3. ANSWERS TO QUIZ ON PAGE 204

1. (i) a poltergeist, (ii) a ghoul, (iii) a doppelganger (or doubleganger), (iv) an author's 'ghost'—not a real (!) ghost, this.

2. (i) Joseph Sheridan Le Fanu, (ii) Dr. M. R. James, (iii) Henry James, (iv) Algernon Blackwood.

3. (i) Eve of May 1st, (ii) at cock-crow, (iii) October 31st, (iv) Midsummer's Eve.

4. (i) Dead of Night, (ii) Blithe Spirit, (iii) Mr. Griggs Returns, (iv) The Scoundrel.

5. (i) Ghost of Hamlet's father, (ii) ghost of old Marley—in Dickens'

Christmas Carol, (iii) ghost of Julius Caesar, (iv) ghost of Banquo—in Macbeth.

6. (i) Irish, (ii) Jewish, (iii) West Indies, especially Haiti, (iv) Scottish.

7. (i) Lay garlic round the doors, windows and chimneys—some people prefer vampires! (ii) stop your ears with wax—its shriek is supposed to bring death to the hearer, (iii) describe a triangle or circle round yourself with a witch hazel rod, (iv) put a bowl of milk or milky porridge outside the door or in the hearth.

8. (i) c, (ii) b, (iii) a, (iv) b.

To Christmas still all English hearts beat true,
And with these words we bid you all

ADIEU

HERE we come a-wassailing
  Among the leaves so green,
Here we come a-wandering,
  So fair to be seen:

Love and joy come to you,
And to you your wassail too,
And God bless you, and send you
A happy new year.

Our wassail cup is made   God bless the master of this house,
  Of the rosemary tree,   Likewise the mistress too;
And so is your beer   And all the little children
  Of the best barley: That round the table go:

And all your kin and kinsfolk,
  That dwell both far and near;
We wish you a Merry Christmas,
  And a happy New Year.

The
WASSAIL SONG

North of England

17th Century